THE
DORSET
LANDSCAPE

Its Scenery and Geology

J*OHN* C*HAFFEY*

DORSET BOOKS

First published in Great Britain in 2004

Frontispiece photograph: *Melbury Hill under snow*

British Library Cataloguing-in-Publication Data
A CIP record for this title is available from the British Library

ISBN 1 871164 43 5

DORSET BOOKS
Official publisher to Dorset County Council

Halsgrove House
Lower Moor Way
Tiverton, Devon EX16 6SS
Tel: 01884 243242
Fax: 01884 243325
email: sales@halsgrove.com
website: www.halsgrove.com

Printed and bound by D'Auria Industrie Grafiche Spa, Italy

CONTENTS

ACKNOWLEDGEMENTS

My thanks are due to my colleagues of the Dorset Geologists' Association Group who first encouraged me to write on the Making of the Dorset Landscape, and for all their valuable discussions on the landscape during many field meetings throughout Dorset. I am also indebted to John Newth, Managing Director of *Dorset Life, The Dorset Magazine* who accepted our offer of articles on the Making of the Dorset Landscape, and who encouraged me to develop an extended series on the subject. The map of the Geology of Dorset is reproduced by permission of the British Geological Survey. © NERC. All rights reserved. IPR/48-6C. As always, my thanks go to my wife Ruth, for all her unfailing help and encouragement in the writing of this book.

SELECTED READING

Allison, Robert J. (Ed), *The Coastal Landforms of West Dorset.* Geologists' Association Guide No. 47, 1992
Bird, Eric, *The Geology and Scenery of Dorset.* Ex Libris Press 1994
Brunsden, D. and Goudie A., *Classic Landforms of the East Dorset Coast.* Geographical Association 1997
Brunsden, D. and Goudie A., *Classic Landforms of the West Dorset Coast.* Geographical Association 1997
Brunsden, D. (Ed), *The Official Guide to the Jurassic Coast.* Coastal Publishing 2003
Burden, R. and Le Pard, G., *A New View of Dorset.* Dorset Books 1996
Chaffey, John, *An Illustrated Guide to the Dorset and East Devon Coast.* Dorset Books 2003
Dorset Geologists' Association Group, *Coast and Country – Geology Walks in and Around Dorset.* 2003
Ensom, Paul, *Discover Dorset – Geology.* Dovecote Press 1998
House, Michael, *Geology of the Dorset Coast.* Geologists' Association Guide 1989

When using this book in the field, the following maps will be of use:
Ordnance Survey : Landranger Series, (1:50,000) Sheets 183 (Yeovil and Frome), 184 (Salisbury and The Plain), 193 (Taunton and Lyme Regis), 194 (Dorchester and Weymouth) and 195 (Bournemouth and Purbeck)
Explore Series (1:25,000) Sheets OL15 (Purbeck and South Dorset), 116 (Lyme Regis and Bridport), 117 (Cerne Abbas and Bere Regis), 118 (Shaftesbury), 129 (Yeovil and Sherborne)
The relevant Geological Survey Sheets 1:50,000 are 312 (Yeovil), 313 (Shaftesbury), 314 (Ringwood), 327 (Bridport), 328 (Dorchester), 329 (Bournemouth), 341 and 342 W (West Fleet and Weymouth), 342E and 343 (Swanage)

Dedication

To the memory of my parents, Charles and Irene Chaffey, who took me on my first trips into Dorset's varied and beautiful landscapes during those distant war-ravaged years of the mid-twentieth century.

INTRODUCTION

For a relatively small county, Dorset possesses an amazing variety of landscapes. Its outstanding coastal landscapes have long been recognised as being of special merit, and most of its length was originally designated as Heritage Coast. More recently, all of the coast from the Devon boundary in the west to Studland in the east was included in the Dorset and East Devon World Heritage Site in 2001. However, it is not only the Dorset Coast, but also much of the interior of the County that displays scenery of such quality that it has been declared part of the Dorset Area of Outstanding Natural Beauty. Some 42% of the County is included within the AONB, extending from Lyme Regis in the west to Blandford in the north-east and to Poole Harbour in the east. In the far north-east of the County, another 9% of Dorset, from Badbury Rings to the Wiltshire border forms part of the Cranborne Chase and West Wiltshire Downs AONB. Even within the middle Frome and Piddle valleys, and the Vale of Blackmoor, that are not part of the AONB, the rural landscape has an instinctive appeal. It is only in the far east of the County that the urban sprawl of the Bournemouth-Poole conurbation has little of the scenic attraction of the landscapes to the west. Even here small patches of heath and pine forest within the urban area hint at a continuous spread of heath between Poole and Christchurch Harbours that existed only 200 years ago.

The coastal landscape owes its immense appeal to the wide variety of rocks and structures that have been shaped by the work of marine erosion and deposition. Great contrasts exist between the far west of the County, with its soaring landslide-riven cliffs between Lyme Regis and Bridport, the gentler shores that fringe Poole and Christchurch Harbours in the east, and the massive limestone cliffs of Portland and the south of Purbeck. Chesil Beach, too, has its own unique presence in the west, bringing an air of both majesty and loneliness to the coast between Chiswell and Burton Bradstock.

Inland Dorset offers many different landscapes; contrasts are often sharp, but sometimes more subtle. The damp lowlands of the Vale of Blackmoor suggest an obvious contrast with the great swathe of Chalkland that sweeps across the County from Eggardon Hill in the west to the Wiltshire borders in the east. Within the Chalk more intimate differences appear, such as those between the high, windswept uplands of Cranborne Chase to the east of Shaftesbury and the lower rolling farm-land around Wimborne and the Allen valley or those between the high uplands around Hardy Monument and the softer contours of the landscape between the Piddle and the North Winterborne. Between Purbeck, with its highly individual landscape, and the central Chalklands lie the rich valley pastures of the Frome and Piddle valleys, where contrast is immediate with the close interplay of the remnants of Egdon Heath and the dark conifer plantations that have too often replaced it. An encircling belt of heathland and mixed wood-land, often dominantly coniferous, shields the rural landscapes from the urban mass of Poole and Bournemouth.

The variety of scenic contrasts within Dorset owes much to the geological basis of the County. Within Dorset there is an almost complete sequence of rocks from early Jurassic times (200 million years ago) to mid-Tertiary times (40 million years ago), as well as the superficial deposits of the

Quaternary period (2 million years ago to the present time). With the designation of the World Heritage Site of the Dorset and East Devon coast in December 2001, the coastal sections of Dorset's geology are becoming increasingly well known, but with limited exposures inland, the geology of much of the County is still unfamiliar to most.

Along the coast, the Jurassic rocks are responsible for much of the stunning scenery of West and South Dorset. Although Cretaceous rocks do appear in the higher parts of the cliffs in West Dorset, it is in East Dorset, especially in Purbeck that rocks of this age, particularly the Chalk, make their maximum impact on the coastal scenery.

In West Dorset, the great landslide complexes of Black Ven and Stonebarrow Hill reflect the cliff sequences of impermeable Lower Jurassic rocks overlain by permeable Cretaceous strata. The stunning yellows and oranges of the cliffs between Bridport and Burton Bradstock owe their outstanding character to the Bridport Sands of the Upper Lias. The limestone cliffs of the Isle of Portland, whether it is in the north, where they brood over past landslide remnants below, or in the south where they drop sheer into deep water, create scenery quite unique within the County. Eastwards, although Portland limestone produces spectacular cliffs around Lulworth Cove and along the south coast of the Isle of Purbeck, it is the soaring white cliffs of the Chalk that appear intermittently from White Nothe as far as Old Harry, that dominate the coastal scene and bestow on it a grandeur unparalleled in southern England. In complete contrast, the dark, almost menacing cliffs on either side of Kimmeridge Bay introduce a different element into the coastal scene. Far away to the east, Dorset's youngest rocks, the Boscombe Sands and the Barton Clay, create a welcome degree of wilderness in the unstable cliffs of Hengistbury Head.

Inland Dorset's geology is dominated, inevitably, by the Chalk, which runs in a great swathe from Wiltshire's Cranborne Chase to its western bastions overlooking the headwaters of Somerset's River Parrett. The Chalk is far from a homogenous rock, and variations in its texture and structure are reflected in subtle changes in the landscape. Harder bands are responsible for features such as Badbury Rings and Pentridge Hill, both of which dominate the surrounding rolling farmland. Although most Chalk scenery is the familiar downland, the hog-back Purbeck Hills are one of Dorset's most impressive sights. Immediately below the Chalk is the Upper Greensand, which, apart from supplying one of Dorset's most mellow building stones, makes an important contribution to scenery in its own right. Around Shaftesbury it builds the high plateau on which the town is built, and southwards forms a striking bench at the foot of the Chalk escarpment on which are sited some of Dorset's most charming villages. In the west of the County, Upper Greensand is responsible for some of Dorset's highest hills and dominant landmarks such as the flat-topped Pilsdon Pen and densely wooded Lewesdon Hill.

If Jurassic rocks are responsible for some of the most spectacular coastal scenery in Dorset, their effect in the interior of the County is essentially more subtle. In the west of the County, Jurassic rocks underlie the Vale of Marshwood and its surrounding hills, and are responsible for the intimate blend of steep-sided hill, plateau and valley that brings such distinctive character to the country around Bridport. In the north of the County, Jurassic rocks underlie the Vale of Blackmoor, but neither the rocks nor scenery possess the degree of uniformity suggested by the name. Jurassic clays such as the Oxford Clay and the Kimmeridge Clay form some of the lowest and dampest land. Corallian rocks form a ridge of higher land, which not only yields a useful building stone in the Todber Freestone, but also provides a dry site for villages such as Wonston, Hazelbury Bryan and Marnhull. Similarly the stony Cornbrash builds a ridge on which the Caundles and Stalbridge have been located. Around Sherborne to the west the middle Jurassic rocks create a series of escarpments which rise tier-on-tier to the Chalk scarp to the south. Sherborne itself, built mostly of the mellow Inferior Oolite, reflects local geology almost more than any other Dorset town.

It is in the east of the County, in the lowlands drained by the Frome and the Piddle that the Tertiary rocks younger than the Chalk outcrop occur. Generally sands and clays, they do not produce striking scenery, although in places they form impressive escarpments overlooking the lowest of the Chalklands, as in the vicinity of Bere Regis. It is the younger Quaternary gravels that form extensive spreads in the Frome and Piddle Valleys and in the Bournemouth and Poole area that make the most significant contribution to the scenery. Much of Hardy's Egdon Heath spreads across the valley gravels east of Dorchester, although it has now been largely replaced by dark conifer plantations, particularly around Puddletown and Wareham. Both Bournemouth and Poole have spread extensively and wantonly across the gravel terraces of the Stour and the ancient Solent River, with only the deeply incised coastal streams and chines bringing variety to their uniform level plateaux.

Although the geology of Dorset has had a profound influence on its physical landscape, it is the agents of erosion and deposition that have been responsible for the shaping of the landscape as we see it today. Weathering, the physical disintegration and chemical decomposition of the rocks, prepares the rocks for the sculpting by rain and rivers and the other erosion agents. After weathering, the resulting material will move downslope to rivers and streams, which will carry it away, either to deposit it further downstream or to transport it to the sea. Most of Dorset's inland landscape displays the evidence of the work of rain and rivers, going back millions of years in some parts of the County, although much of the landscape is far younger. Rain and rivers have been largely responsible for the eroding away of the softer rocks that underlie lowland areas such as the Vale of Blackmoor, the

valleys of the Frome and the Piddle, the Vale of Marshwood and the claylands around Weymouth. The great sweep of Chalk uplands forms most of the higher land within the County, simply because the permeable Chalk is eroded more slowly by the agents of erosion, particularly since much of the area has not carried surface drainage since the end of the Ice Age.

Although Dorset did not carry any permanent ice cover during the Pleistocene, or Ice Age, the area did experience a periglacial climate, similar to that experienced today in Alaska, northern Canada and the northern latitudes of Europe and Asia. Under such conditions weathered surface material moves downslope during the brief summer, even though the ground at depth is permanently frozen – a feature known as permafrost.

Coastal erosion and deposition have shaped the rocks exposed along the coast to form some of the most spectacular scenery in the country. Since sea levels changed often during the Ice Age, the coast exhibits a range of features that reflect this instability. Many of the principal features of the coast that we see today may well have originated during the Pleistocene, and the present work of the sea may only be modifying landforms that have been inherited from an earlier stage of coastal evolution. However, some of the most stunning landforms, such as Durdle Door, and the erosion complex at Handfast Point near Studland, are clearly the work of contemporary activity. Major features such as Chesil Beach have, inevitably, a much more complex history. It is important to remember, however, that features such as our beaches see almost daily change, resulting from the constant modifying work of waves, currents and tides working ceaselessly together.

So the work of the agents of erosion and deposition operating on the underlying geology have produced the physical landscape of Dorset as we see it today. It is convenient, for the purposes of this book to divide the landscapes of the County into seven distinct units. Six different landscapes may be distinguished in the interior of the County. The Chalklands inevitably dominate the interior, with their landscapes of rolling downland, seamed with dry valleys, spectacular escarpments and the attractive through river valleys with their damp water meadows. To the north lies the landscape of North Dorset, dominated by the lowlands of the Vale of Blackmoor. Beyond the western bastions of the Chalklands are the great Greensand hills of West Dorset, that tower above the claylands of the Vale of Marshwood. Around Bournemouth and Poole and extending westwards into the Frome and Piddle Valleys is a landscape dominated by gravel terraces and patches of lowland developed on sands and clays. The dramatic scenery of Purbeck, with its high Chalk ridge, its heathlands and its limestone plateaux, borne of the juxtaposition of a wide variety of rocks gives the area a distinct identity. South Dorset, essentially the hinterland of Weymouth, also has its own intimate landscape of lowland and steep-sided hills. Finally the magnificent coast of the County forms a maritime fringe of infinite variety along the three great bays of Lyme, Weymouth and Poole.

The Chalk cliffs of Purbeck – looking south from The Foreland

✑ 1 ✑
THE GEOLOGY OF DORSET

Dorset's geology reveals an almost complete sequence of rocks from early Jurassic times (200 million years ago) to mid–Tertiary times (40 million years ago). Younger superficial deposits, such as river gravels and flood plain silts, belonging to the Quaternary period, have been laid down in the last 2 million years, and are much more widely distributed in the County than the rocks belonging to older periods. Broadly speaking, the oldest of Dorset's rocks outcrop in the west of the County, and they become increasingly younger in age towards the east of the County. This is particularly well displayed along the coast, where the oldest rocks (Lower Jurassic) appear in the west in the cliffs at Lyme Regis, and the youngest (mid–Tertiary) are found outcropping in the cliffs at Hengistbury Head and Highcliffe in the extreme east of the County. Inland there is a broadly similar picture, with the oldest Jurassic rocks underlying the Vale of Blackmoor on the Somerset border and the youngest appearing in the Bournemouth area, with a decline in age from north-west to south-east. This simple pattern is somewhat complicated by the fact that great earth movements in mid–Tertiary times have disturbed the rocks in the south of Dorset. There the rocks have been folded, faulted and often contorted to give an irregular pattern of outcrop in the Weymouth and Purbeck areas.

The Lower Jurassic strata or Lias (derived from the quarrymen's pronunciation of 'layers') are the oldest of Dorset's Jurassic rocks. They outcrop in West Dorset in the cliffs between Lyme Regis and Burton Bradstock, and inland they floor the Vale of Marshwood. On the coast the cliffs that they form are often capped by the golden coloured Upper Greensand as at Golden Cap, Stonebarrow Hill and Thorncombe Beacon. The Lower Lias consists of dark shales, interbedded with thin bands of limestone, well seen in Church Cliffs to the east of Lyme Regis. These rocks, laid down in deep water lacking in oxygen, are particularly rich in fossils, including ammonites, belemnites, bivalves and a rich fauna of fish and reptiles. Mary Anning (1799–1847), probably the most famous early fossil collector, earned a living from the fossils she obtained from these rocks. The succeeding Middle Lias, which outcrops in the middle section of the cliffs of Golden Cap and also in Thorncombe Beacon, consists of clays, silts and sandstones that were laid down in rather shallower water, where conditions were often stormy. The Upper Lias, superbly displayed in East Cliff, West Bay, and in Burton Cliff farther to the east, is repre-

Lower Lias – The Belemnite Marls, cliffs east of Charmouth

Upper Lias – Bridport Sands, Burton Cliff

appears in the north-west of Dorset, and forms a notable escarpment to the south and east of Sherborne. The Upper Fuller's Earth Clay, now renamed the Frome Clay is well exposed in Watton Cliff to the west of West Bay, and appears again in the heart of the Weymouth lowland to the east. It occurs in a wide belt in north Dorset from Thornford eastwards towards Milborne Port. The overlying Forest Marble, deposited in shallower water than the Fuller's Earth, is not a true marble, but a shelly limestone that takes a good polish. It outcrops in a coastal escarpment that runs from Abbotsbury to Burton Bradstock, again in the Weymouth lowland, and in a complicated belt in North Dorset that runs from near Rampisham north-eastwards to near Henstridge just over the Somerset border.

sented largely by the Bridport Sands. Inland these sands can be traced northwards through Melplash and Netherbury and eventually cross the Somerset border, and become the Yeovil Sands. In the sunken lanes that characterise this belt of country the harder bands stand out as prominent projections where they have proved more resistant to erosion. In the east of the County, the Bridport Sands form one of the important reservoirs at depth in the Wytch Farm oilfield.

Middle Jurassic Rocks in Dorset commence with the Inferior Oolite, which is only a few feet thick at the coast, but increases to nearly 70 feet (21 metres) near Sherborne, where it is of sufficiently good quality to be used extensively as a building stone. The Inferior Oolite was laid down in a relatively shallow sea, which encouraged the formation of the tiny spherical ooliths that make up the body of the rock. Each tiny oolith was formed from the deposition of successive layers of calcium carbonate around a nucleus of a sand grain or shell fragment. Succeeding strata were deposited in deeper, muddier water. The Fuller's Earth Clays take their name from the fact that this material was often used in the past for degreasing wool; it probably originated as an ash-fall from a volcanic eruption to the west. Immediately above this horizon a thin rubbly limestone, the Fuller's Earth Rock,

Succeeding the Forest Marble is the thin rubbly limestone known as the Cornbrash – its name being derived from the thin brashy soils on which corn was grown. It was again deposited in a relatively shallow sea, and its well-drained outcrop forms an ideal site for villages in the Vale of Blackmoor, such as Yetminster, Stalbridge and the Caundles. In the south of the County it outcrops in the centre of the Weymouth lowland, and also in a belt that runs east–west along the Bride valley. Deepening of the sea saw the deposition of the Kellaways Beds, mostly shales and overlying sandstones, well exposed in the disused brick pits at Chickerell. These beds may be traced westwards into the Bride valley, and in the north of the County they form low-lying ground around Leigh and Chetnole. Above is the Oxford Clay with a thickness of about 750 feet (230 metres). It forms much of the low-lying ground in the Weymouth lowland, and occurs again in the Bride Valley to the west. In the north of the County it underlies much of the damp lowland of Blackmoor Vale.

Dorset's Upper Jurassic sequence begins with the Corallian rocks. They were deposited in water that once again had shallowed, and consist mainly of sandstones, clays and lime-

GEOLOGY MAP OF DORSET

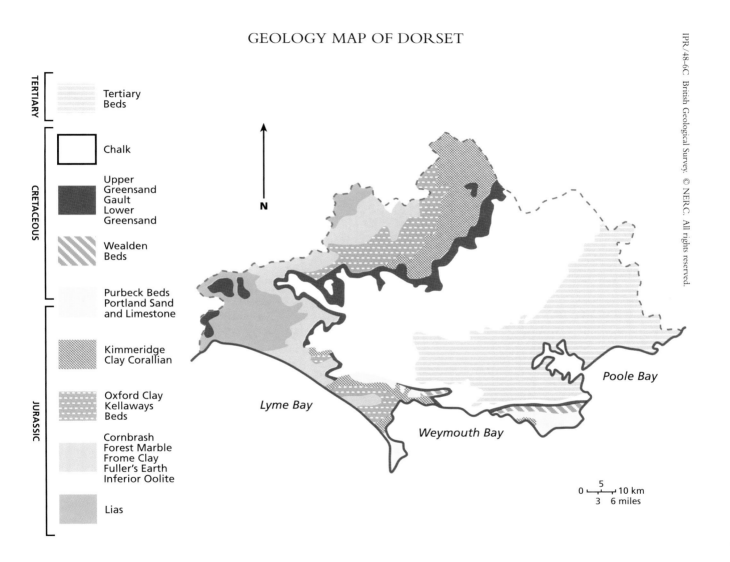

TERTIARY

Tertiary
Beds

CRETACEOUS

Chalk

Upper
Greensand
Gault
Lower
Greensand

Wealden
Beds

Purbeck Beds
Portland Sand
and Limestone

JURASSIC

Kimmeridge
Clay Corallian

Oxford Clay
Kellaways
Beds

Cornbrash
Forest Marble
Frome Clay
Fuller's Earth
Inferior Oolite

Lias

N

Lyme Bay

Weymouth Bay

Poole Bay

0   5   10 km
   3   6 miles

Corallian rocks– Bran Point, Ringstead

Kimmeridge Clay – coast east from Rope Lake Head

stones. The sandstones and limestones suggest particularly shallow water, with the clays representing episodes of deeper conditions. Corallian rocks outcrop in two main areas of Dorset. In the south they appear between Abbotsbury and Osmington to the north of Weymouth, and around Wyke Regis to the south of Weymouth. In the north of the County, they form a low ridge that extends from Mappowder in the south through Sturminster Newton to Cucklington, once again providing dry sites for the location of settlements.

The Kimmeridge Clay is one of Dorset's most interesting sequences. It is best exposed on the Purbeck coast to the east and west of Kimmeridge itself, but also makes an appearance on the northern edge of the Weymouth lowland. In the north of the County it forms a low-lying belt in the Vale of Blackmoor, largely devoid of villages because of the damp soils. The Kimmeridge Clay has a total thickness of over nearly 1600 feet (490 metres), and is made up of clays and shales, laid down in deep, oxygen-deficient water. This environment caused the death of many of the organisms and encouraged their preservation, so the strata are richly fossil-iferous. Oil shales in the Kimmeridge Clay have been used

as fuel in the past, even for boiling sea water to produce salt. Kimmeridge was the site of a number of industrial ventures in the past, including alum and glass production, and the distillation of oil from the shale. Interestingly, Kimmeridge Clay underneath the North Sea has been buried deeply enough for it to be the source of much of its oil, but the rocks in Dorset have never been buried deeply enough for oil to be formed.

The succeeding Portland Sand and Portland Limestone have a much more restricted outcrop being confined to a belt in the south of the Isle of Purbeck, a zone along the northern edge of the Weymouth lowland and the Isle of Portland. A shallowing of the sea after the deposition of the Kimmeridge Clay led to the accumulation of the Portland Sand.

Above the Portland Sand, the Portland Limestone was also deposited in shallow water. In the upper part of the Portland Limestone are valuable building stones, used for many public buildings in London and in other cities in the United Kingdom, and for the United Nations Building in New York and the Government Buildings in New Delhi.

Portland Limestone – St Aldhelm's Head

Controversy has long existed as to the proper dividing line between the Jurassic Period and the succeeding Cretaceous within the Purbeckian sequence. Opinion now seems to favour a position just above the Portland Limestone, so that most of the Purbeck sequence lies within the Cretaceous System. Conditions saw a marked change in the Purbeckian, for most of the rock sequence seems to have been deposited in shallow coastal lagoons and freshwater lakes, although the sea did invade this environment occasionally. Most of the rocks are limestones, shales and clays with occasional fossil soils in which the trees of the Fossil Forest at Lulworth grew. The famous Purbeck Marble, widely used in churches in Purbeck is in fact a shelly limestone, made of thousands of tiny snail shells, that takes a good polish and can be used for decorative work.

The succeeding Wealden Beds consist of a series of multi-coloured sands, sandstones, clays and grits. They outcrop in a belt from Swanage Bay to Worbarrow Bay in the Isle of Purbeck, and appear briefly around Chaldon and Upton

Purbeck Beds – Fossil Forest, east of Lulworth Cove

farther to the west. These beds were laid down by rivers that drained into the area from the west and the north, and rock and mineral fragments within the sequence suggest that they may have been eroded from the Cornubian uplands to the west.

Marine conditions succeeded the deposition of the Wealden Beds, and led to the deposition of the Lower Greensand, named from the green mineral, glauconite, that occurs within the rock. Its outcrop is virtually limited to the Isle of Purbeck in a narrow belt from Punfield Cove north of Swanage to just west of Lulworth. It makes only a brief appearance in the north of the County near Child Okeford. Above the Lower Greensand lies the Gault, a stiff blue clay. Its much wider occurrence indicates a continuing major transgression of the sea at this time. Lying beneath the permeable Upper Greensand and Chalk, the impermeable Gault is often instrumental in causing landslides, both in coastal locations and in the interior as for instance around Shaftesbury. The succeeding Upper Greensand consists of sands, sandstones and beds of the resistant chert. It forms a capping to the great tabular hills of West Dorset such as Pilsdon Pen, some of West Dorset's most spectacular cliffs

such as Golden Cap, and an important bench at the foot of the Chalk escarpment from Shaftesbury southwards.

Chalk has the most extensive outcrop of any of Dorset's rocks, and dominates the scenery of much of the interior of the County, as well as forming some of its most stunning cliff scenery. Although the lowest parts of the Chalk sequence do contain gritty material in the west of the County and other finer land-derived material elsewhere, giving a grey, marly appearance, much of the Chalk is formed of the remains of microscopic marine organisms, which are responsible for its fine, white texture. Within the Chalk there are important bands of flint, which become increasingly numerous towards the top. These flint bands are derived initially from siliceous organisms that lived in the Chalk seas. Flint survives much longer than the remainder of the Chalk and is thus an important and vital constituent of many of Dorset's beaches.

Uplift and erosion of the Chalk was followed by the deposition of the succeeding Tertiary Beds, which include sediments laid down in rivers, estuaries and the sea. The Lower Tertiary Beds are quite well represented in East Dorset, but the Upper Tertiary is largely missing. The youngest Tertiary

Poole Formation – Broadstone Sand, Redend Point, Studland

Beds are usually brightly coloured clays, which were even used for brick-making in places. The succeeding London Clay was laid down under marine conditions, whilst the Bracklesham Group of beds, which underlie much of East Dorset's heathlands, bears evidence of deposition in rivers that flowed into the area from the west. Dorset's youngest Tertiary Beds indicate a further return to marine conditions, with the Barton Clay being particularly prominent in the cliffs at Hengistbury Head and Highcliffe.

Although the ice sheets that covered much of Britain during Pleistocene (Ice Age) times did not reach Dorset, snow fields and possibly small ice caps would have existed on the highest parts of the Dorset Downs. Frost shattering would have been prevalent on the surface, with the angular debris forming prominent screes at the foot of cliffs on the coast. At depth, permafrost would have indicated that the ground was permanently frozen. Late spring and early summer melting would have encouraged powerful streams to carry frost-shattered debris, down into the broad river valleys such as the Frome, the Piddle and the Stour. Here this material would have been deposited as broad spreads of gravel and sand that were later dissected into terraces as the rivers continued to cut down to sea level.

Barton Clay, capped with Quaternary Gravels – Hengistbury Head

Frost shattered solifluction debris – West Hill Bottom, Kingston

Finer grained material, known as Brickearth, found capping the cliffs between Mudeford and Highcliffe in the east of Dorset is probably a wind-blown deposit. Once glacial deposits farther to the north had been exposed at the surface after the ice had melted, the finest material would have been winnowed away by winds, and it would have been carried southwards to be deposited as Brickearth.

The Geological Structure of Dorset

The rocks of southern Dorset have been much affected by the mid-Tertiary earth movements caused when Africa collided with Europe, creating the Alps in the process. Two major upfold structures dominate the Dorset coast, the Weymouth anticline in the west and the Purbeck monocline in the east. They are complemented inland by a major downfold, the Frome syncline. The Weymouth anticline is an asymmetrical structure, with gentle dips on the south in the Isle of Portland, and much steeper dips on the north. This northern limb is further complicated by a series of minor folds and a major fault system. The Purbeck monocline is also asymmetrical where rocks on the northern limb are either steeply dipping or overturned as along the coast between Worbarrow Bay and Durdle Door. Within the Frome syncline the youngest Tertiary rocks of Dorset are preserved. The Chalk of the Dorset Downs dips gently southeast towards the Frome syncline, only to reappear, steeply dipping to the north, in the Purbeck Hills to the south.

⤺ 2 ⤻
THE SHAPING OF THE DORSET LANDSCAPE

Dorset's landscape reflects not only the nature of the underlying geology but also the physical forces at work that shape the landscape. As a result of their chemical composition and their physical make-up rocks will react differently to the processes that are responsible for their breakdown and erosion. In order to be worn down, rocks have firstly to be weathered, by disintegration or decomposition. Weathered debris is moved downslope by a variety of processes, and is then transported away by the various agents of erosion. In simple terms, rocks that are resistant to weathering and erosion will form the higher land in any area, and thus in Dorset, the Chalk and limestones tend to stand out above the softer clays and sands that are also important in the County's geology. Over millions of years Dorset's landscape has been shaped by the action of rain and rivers, and it is the work of these agents that is most evident in the nature of the landscape. However, during the relatively recent Ice Age, although Dorset did not carry a cover of ice, it did experience a very cold periglacial climate, and processes that operated during this time have left their mark on the landscape. Currently, rain and rivers, and the action of the sea, are continuing the fashioning of the landforms and scenery of the County.

Igneous rocks (those that have cooled from the molten state), and metamorphic rocks (those that have been altered, and usually hardened, by heat or pressure) are normally the most resistant to erosion, and tend to form the highest land. Dorset's geology does not include either of these rock types, but is made up entirely of sedimentary rocks (that are formed of the debris resulting from the erosion of other rocks, and are usually found in layers). It is the different reactions of these sedimentary rocks to the processes of weathering and erosion that are responsible for the major features of the scenery of Dorset. Generally speaking, Chalk and other limestones, such as the Portland Limestone in the south of the County and the thinner limestones of the Corallian and Cornbrash in both the north and the south, form land which is higher than that floored by the softer clays and sands that are also widely distributed in Dorset. Thus Dorset's highest country is underlain by the Chalk, that sweeps across the County from Cranborne Chase almost to the Devon border. Portland Limestone, with a cover of the Purbeck Beds, forms the small high blocks of the Isle of Portland and the southern part of the Isle of Purbeck. In the north of the County both the Cornbrash and the Corallian form low ridges by virtue of their greater resistance to erosion than the surrounding clays.

Weathering is the process by which rocks are broken down, either physically through disintegration, chemically, through decomposition, or biologically though the action of plants and animals. Rocks can disintegrate through alternate heating and cooling, with the expansion and contraction causing stresses within the rock that eventually lead to its breakdown. The action of frost in rock breakdown has been particularly important in Dorset. Water in joints (major fractures in rocks) and pores can expand on freezing, and the consequent pressure can result in the fracture of rocks. Large scale accumulations of scree, such as at the base of St Aldhelm's Head in Purbeck, have resulted from such action in periglacial times.

Periglacial screes at the foot of St Aldhelm's Head

Landslide – Ringstead

Chemical decomposition of rocks results from the operation of a number of processes. Limestone in particular can decompose as a result of the action of slightly acidic rainwater on calcium carbonate, converting it to calcium bicarbonate, which can be removed in solution. This is particularly important in the formation of caves, and other solution features. Sometimes downward percolating water derived from acidic surface vegetation, such as heathland, can result in the decomposition and solution of the Chalk, as in the dolines on Bronkham Hill and the larger hollows such as Culpepper's Dish. Roots of trees extending down into the joints within rocks can also be responsible for their widening and the consequent breakdown of rocks. This is often clearly seen in cliff sections as around Redend Point at Studland.

Once rocks have been broken down by weathering, the resulting debris can then be removed by gravity-induced downslope movement, either on cliff faces at the coast, or valley slopes inland. Downslope movement is known as mass movement, and it occurs in many different ways. The slow imperceptible movement of surface debris on valley slopes is known as soil creep. Much more spectacular are the

more rapid movements such as rockfalls and landslides. The great rockfall at Mupe Bay in spring 2001 brought thousands of tons of Chalk down on to the beach and brought about a fundamental change in the profile of the bay. Similarly, large scale landslides are characteristic of much of the high cliff faces of West Dorset such as Black Ven and Stonebarrow Hill. Here great blocks of material slide downwards along a curved surface, and tilt backwards as they move, often giving a stepped profile to the cliffs.

Once weathered material has been carried downslope it reaches a river or stream, which is then capable of moving this debris downstream, providing that it has enough energy. The debris can be carried away in different ways: soluble material is carried away in solution; the finer material is carried in suspension, which gives Dorset's rivers a muddy appearance after heavy rain; coarser fragments are either bounced along the bed of the river or, in the case of the largest fragments, dragged along the bed. Rivers rarely flow in a straight line, and even Dorset's smallest streams tend to flow in meandering curves. The meandering habit is best seen, however, in some of Dorset's longer streams, such as the Frome, the Piddle and the Stour.

Rivers carry their load down towards the sea, and in times of flood they will extend their flow on to the surrounding valley floor. Here the energy of the river will decrease and some of the load will be deposited on the so-called flood-plain, gradually building it up. In the lower part of the course of the Piddle, the Frome and the Stour, the rivers meander across a broad flood plain. If sea level fluctuates, as it frequently did in the Ice Age, rivers will react to these

Left: *Interlocking spurs, caused by a meandering stream (the valley is now dry) — Melbury Bottom, Ashmore, North Dorset*

Below: *Meanders — River Stour, near Sturminster Newton*

changes. If sea level falls, as when water is extracted from the oceans to form ice sheets, then rivers will adjust their course and cut down into their floodplains, leaving old floodplain gravels at a previous level forming river terraces. Such terraces are striking features of the river scenery on all three of Dorset's main rivers. St Catherine's Hill, north of Christchurch, is a high level terrace remnant, and around Wool the terraces of the Frome form a staircase leading up to the higher land around Gallows Hill. When sea level rises the lower parts of a river's course will be flooded, to form estuaries such as Christchurch and Poole Harbours. Debris carried into these estuaries by rivers will result in their slowly silting up.

Along the coast marine activity is responsible for eroding rock material away from cliff faces and transporting it either along the shore or offshore. The forces of waves will loosen the rock structure at the base of cliffs, and it will be further weakened by waves throwing debris against the cliff, often breaking fragments away. Thus rock debris accumulates at the base of the cliff, and it is worn down by waves dragging it backwards and forwards. This attritional movement will also wear away the rocks beneath, forming a wave-cut plat-

form, well seen around Redend Point at Studland, and at the base of the Chalk cliffs west of Durdle Door, although here it is often obscured by beach debris.

Where lines of weakness exist in the rocks of the cliff, they will be exploited by marine erosion, and caves will form, as on the western end of Durdle Cove, where a series of caves have been formed along a low angle fault. On headlands caves can be driven in from both sides and eventually a breakthrough is achieved, and an arch will form. Dorset's most spectacular arch is Durdle Door, but smaller caves running right through a headland can be seen at Bat's Hole under Bat's Head west of Durdle Door, and at Handfast Point near Old Harry. When the keystone of an arch collapses, a stack such as Old Harry will form, and eventually, under wave attack, topple over, to leave a stump, such as Old Harry's Wife. Several stumps can be seen to the west of Durdle Door marking the western extension of the Portland Limestone.

Beach debris is carried parallel to the shoreline by a process called longshore drift. Waves breaking oblique to the shore-line will carry pebbles and sand up the beach with their own momentum. As the wave retreats, the backwash will move

River Terraces – St Catherine's Hill, near Christchurch

Wave-cut platform – near Swyre Head, west of Durdle Door

Caves cut along low angle fault, Durdle Cove

Bat's Hole, small cave cutting through Bat's Head, with Butter Rock, a stack cut in Chalk

down the beach at right angles, under gravity, carrying the material with it. With each movement of the waves the material moves a little further along the shore. When a break in the shoreline occurs as, for instance, at an estuary, the material will be carried out into the estuary and eventually be built up by waves to form a spit.

Mudeford Sandspit has been built out across the combined estuary of the Stour and Avon from material carried around Hengistbury Head from the south-west.

Periglacial conditions probably affected Dorset for much of the Ice Age from 2 million years ago, until the last ice melted about 10,000 years ago. During this time much of Dorset would have been under a permafrost regime, where the ground is frozen to some depth. One effect of the permafrost is to render rocks such as Chalk and limestones impermeable. Normally these rocks, on account of their well-jointed nature, will allow the downward passage of water. Once the water in the joints and pores of the rocks becomes frozen, it renders the rock impermeable, and thus streams can flow across the surface, albeit briefly, in the short

periglacial summer, often cutting quite deep valleys such as Giant's Grave Bottom, north of Swanage. Thus the Chalk supported an intricate drainage network in periglacial times; however, once the permafrost melted at the end of the Ice Age, the rocks became permeable again and the present pattern of dry valleys in the Chalk, such a characteristic feature of the Dorset Downs, became established.

During the brief periglacial summers the surface layers of the permafrost would melt, forming the so-called active layer. When these layers became saturated with the water that had thawed out, they had a tendency to move downs-lope, a process known as solifluction. Today in many of Dorset's valleys it is possible to see solifluction lobes where this material had moved downwards, and solifluction terraces can sometimes be seen on the side of valleys. Cross-sections of soliflucted debris are visible where dry valleys meet the coast; a particularly good example is at the seaward end of Scratchy Bottom just west of Durdle Door. Frost action produced great screes at the foot of Dorset's cliffs during periglacial times, such as at the base of the cliffs along the northern edge of the Isle of Portland.

Dorset's landscape thus reflects the intricate interplay of the variations in its geology and the processes that have operated on it in the past and continue to do so today. The infinite variety of the landscape, from the majestic Chalk heights on the borders of Cranborne Chase to the heath and pine covered terraces of the Frome and the Piddle, from the great coastal bastions of White Nothe and Houns-tout to the broad sweep of Studland's sand dunes, all bear witness to the constant change being wrought by the action of the physical processes that have shaped it.

Cliffs cut in the Wealden Beds, Mupe Bay

❧ 3 ❧
THE LANDSCAPE REGIONS OF DORSET

Broadly speaking Dorset's variety of landscapes can be grouped together into six landscape regions, with the coast forming a distinctive seventh:

- North Dorset
- The Chalklands
- East Dorset
- West Dorset
- South Dorset
- The Isle of Purbeck
- The Coast

North Dorset

This region is dominated by the damp pastures of Blackmoor Vale, floored by the Kimmeridge Clay in the east and the Oxford Clay in the west, and drained by the Stour and its two principal tributaries the Lodden and the Lydden. Separating the two clay outcrops is a ridge formed by the Corallian rocks. Westwards the Cornbrash forms another low ridge before the outcrop of the Inferior Oolite around Sherborne is encountered. Northwards from Sherborne, the Yeovil Sands form low plateau country. Immediately below the Chalk escarpment to the east and the south, the Upper Greensand forms an important bench, another dry site for village location.

The Chalklands

The rolling Chalk downland is the largest landscape region in Dorset. It is bounded on the north by the great escarpment that runs almost uninterrupted from the Wiltshire border to Winyard's Gap and Seaborough Hill, and then swings back on

North Dorset: Blackmoor Vale under snow, from Fontmell Down

Chalklands: cultivated Chalkland, north of Badbury Rings

THE LANDSCAPE REGIONS

N

NORTH DORSET

CHALKLANDS

WEST DORSET

EAST DORSET

THE COAST

SOUTH DORSET

ISLE OF PURBECK

0   5   10 km
    3   6 miles

itself to form the heights of Eggardon and Black Down, and eventually reaches the sea at White Nothe. From the crest of the escarpment the Chalklands decrease in height to the south and east until the Chalk dips down below the Tertiary sands and clays that are found in the Frome, Piddle and Stour valleys and the belt of lowland that links them. Thus the Chalklands are a series of downland blocks that are separated by the valleys of major streams that flow across the outcrop of the Chalk. Only the Stour maintains a course that has its origins to the north of the Chalk; the other streams, the Frome and the Piddle, rise within the Chalk outcrop near the northern escarpment. Apart from these valleys, the Chalklands are dissected by an intricate network of dry valleys that were almost certainly much deepened in periglacial times.

East Dorset

Of all of the landscape regions of Dorset, East Dorset has the least imposing scenery. The Tertiary rocks of sand and clay that underlie the region are not resistant to erosion, and thus form low-lying farmland and pastures. The Quaternary gravels deposited by the Stour and the ancient Solent River form extensive plateaux over which the urban areas of Bournemouth and Poole have spread, and similar terraces extend westwards up the valleys of the Frome and the Piddle to form gravel 'staircases' leading up to the Chalklands to the north and the Isle of Purbeck to the south.

East Dorset: Christchurch Harbour from Hengistbury Head

West Dorset

Two main elements dominate the scenery of West Dorset. The low-lying Vale of Marshwood occupies the centre of the region, underlain by the damp clays of the Lias.

Rising loftily above the intricate pastures and hedgerows of the Vale are the Greensand capped hills of Coney's Castle, Lambert's Hill, Pilsdon Pen and Lewesdon Hill. To the east of the Vale of Marshwood, the Bridport Sands and Inferior Oolite create a landscape of steep-sided hills and deeply incised valleys in a stretch of country that extends from Powerstock to Bridport.

West Dorset: Hardown Hill from Golden Cap

South Dorset

The smallest of the landscape regions embraces all of the Weymouth lowland south of the Chalk escarpment that runs from above Abbotsbury in the west to north of Osmington in the east, and the isolated limestone block of the Isle of Portland. Low east-west limestone ridges formed of the Portland Limestone, the Corallian and the Cornbrash diversify the lowland, where the Oxford and Kimmeridge Clays form the lowest ground.

South Dorset: Weymouth Lowland from Hardy Monument

The Isle of Purbeck

Purbeck has its own distinctive assemblage of landscapes within a relatively small area. In the north are the low-lying heathlands, a vegetation response to the infertile sands and clays of the Poole formation. The region has its own narrow and open Chalk ridge, quite different from the broad spreads of downland in the centre and north of the County. Beyond the hogback of the Chalk ridge is the central vale, developed on the Wealden Beds, running from Swanage Bay in the east to Worbarrow Bay in the west. Purbeck's own limestone plateau forms a block to the south of the vale, almost hiding the tiny Kimmeridge lowland in the southwest.

Above: *The Isle of Purbeck: Corfe Castle and the western Purbeck Hills*

Right: *The Coast: Durdle Door*

The Coast

The coast effectively cuts across five of the other landscape regions, but merits its inclusion as a separate entity, with its own maritime character. On account of its clear and invaluable record of 160 million years of geological time, its stunning scenery, its secure place in the development of geology as a science, and its potential for future research, most of it is now a World Heritage Site. Few stretches of coastline of equivalent length show such variety of geology and scenery. West Dorset displays its great cliffs of Black Ven, Stonebarrow and Golden Cap. Chesil Beach has its own unique character as a shingle structure unequalled in Western Europe. South Dorset and Purbeck exhibit an amazing variety of intricate cliff and bay scenery. The east of the Dorset coastline, if encumbered by urban development, boasts two of the finest estuarine environments in Britain, on either side of the Bournemouth-Poole conurbation.

❧ 4 ❧
THE LANDSCAPE SITES

Within the seven different landscape regions, 70 outstanding landscape sites have been chosen for detailed description and explanation. All 70 sites are shown on the map, and they are described alphabetically under each landscape region. Inevitably, regions such as the Chalklands, and also the coast, display the largest number of chosen sites. This is to a certain degree a reflection of their extent, but it also shows that the most spectacular scenery in Dorset is not confined to the coast. The exceptional landforms revealed along the Chalk escarpment make a major contribution to Dorset's inland landscapes. The large number of sites shown in the Isle of Purbeck indicates that it displays some of the finest scenery in the County, a reflection of the wide variations in its geology.

St Oswald's Bay, west of Lulworth Cove

THE LANDSCAPE SITES

North Dorset
1   Birts Hill
2   Blackmoor Vale
3   Duncliffe Hill
4   The Sherborne Escarpments

The Chalklands
5   Badbury Rings
6   Black Down
7   Bronkham Hill
8   Bulbarrow and Woolland Hills
9   The Cliff, Blandford
10 Compton Valence
11 Dogbury Hill
12 The Dorsetshire Gap
13 Eggardon Hill
14 Hambledon Hill
15 The High Valleys of Cranborne Chase
16 Longcombe Bottom
17 Lyscombe Bottom
18 Melbury Hill
19 Pentridge Hill
20 The Sydling-Cerne Downlands
21 The Valley of Stones
22 Winyard's Gap

East Dorset
23 Beacon Hill
24 The Bournemouth Chines
25 Brownsea Island
26 Culpepper's Dish
27 Gallows Hill
28 St Catherine's Hill
29 Stanpit Marshes
30 Woodbury Hill

West Dorset
31 Abbotsbury Castle
32 The Bridport Hills
33 Chapel Hill
34 The Knoll
35 Pilsdon Pen

36 Seaborough Hill
37 Shipton Hill
38 The Vale of Marshwood

South Dorset
39 Chalbury Hill
40 Friar Waddon and Corton Hills
41 The Sutton Poyntz Lowland

The Isle of Purbeck
42 The Agglestone
43 The Cocknowle Gap
44 Corfe Castle
45 Corfe Common
46 Creechbarrow
47 The East Chaldon Valley
48 Giant's Grave Bottom
49 The Golden Bowl
50 Hartland Moor .
51 The Purbeck 'Gwyles'
52 Redcliffe

Coastal sites
53 Black Ven
54 Golden Cap
55 Chesil Beach
56 The Fleet
57 Portland Bill
58 Redcliff Point
59 White Nothe
60 Scratchy Bottom
61 The Lulworth Coast
62 Gad Cliff
63 The Kimmeridge Coast and The Ledges
64 Chapman's Pool
65 Peveril Point
66 Old Harry and The Pinnacles
67 Studland Dunes
68 Little Sea
69 Hengistbury Head
70 Mudeford Sandspit

NORTH DORSET

Birts Hill

This prominent hill lies astride the boundary between Dorset and Somerset, and dominates the low-lying country to the north-west and south-east of its wooded slopes. Both Birts Hill and the neighbouring Abbotts Hill are a part of a belt of shelly limestone, the Forest Marble, that runs north-eastwards towards Sherborne. Much of the surrounding low-lying land is floored with the relatively easily erodible Fuller's Earth or Frome Clay, drained by the Broad River in Somerset and the Corscombe streams in Dorset, that drain northwards into the Sutton Bingham Reservoir, and eventually into the River Yeo near Yeovil. Birts Hill is now largely tree-covered, and its partly-wooded summit is capped with an outlier of the thin rubbly limestone known as the Cornbrash. Its long smooth

Birts Hill

slopes are relatively unscarred by landslips, in marked contrast to the tumbled and broken landscape below the Chalk of Winyard's Gap to the south-west. At one time Birts Hill was continuous with Abbotts Hill to the north and Ashland Hill to the south-west. Tiny streams from both the Somerset side and the Dorset slopes have cut back into the former ridge, and have now effectively isolated Birts Hill from the other two features.

Blackmoor Vale

Blackmoor Vale, extending roughly from Gillingham in the north to Yetminster in the southwest, is one of the largest tracts of low-lying land in Dorset. Thomas Hardy referred to it in *Tess of the D'Urbervilles* as 'The Vale of Little Dairies', a name which epitomises the intimate patchwork of enclosed lush pastures and close network of small farms that lie at the foot of the great Chalk escarpment that runs from Melbury Hill to Bubb Down. It is floored by the Kimmeridge Clay to the southeast and by the Oxford Clay to the northwest, the two outcrops being separated by the low limestone ridge of the Corallian Beds that runs from Buckhorn Weston to Hazelbury Bryan.

Both the Kimmeridge Clay and the Oxford Clay are impermeable and give rise to a dense network of small streams that drain into the Stour in the east and into the Yeo in the west. The Stour and its tributaries drain eventually into Christchurch Bay and the English Channel, whilst the Yeo and its tributaries drain into Bridgwater Bay and the Bristol Channel. The watershed that separates the two different

Blackmoor Vale

drainage systems runs imperceptibly from High Stoy Hill through Longburton towards the Caundles.

The Kimmeridge Clay and the Oxford Clay both give rise to damp, ill-drained and often intractable soils. Place names such as Margaret Marsh and Guy's Marsh are testimony to the poor drainage of much of the vale. Many of the larger villages, such as Marnhull, have therefore been built on the higher and drier ground of the limestones of the Corallian, or, in the case of Stalbridge, on the limestone of the Cornbrash. It is thus the succession of clay lowlands that make up Blackmoor Vale, together with the intervening limestone ridges, that contribute so much to the intricate variety of the North Dorset landscape.

Duncliffe Hill

Duncliffe Hill, some 2½ miles (4km) west of Shaftesbury, is best seen from the great sweep of Chalk Downs that take in

Melbury Hill and Fontmell Down. From the summit of Melbury Hill, neighbouring Shaftesbury can be seen, built on a high plateau of Upper Greensand, with its steep slopes falling away to the west and the north. The Upper Greensand consists of the Shaftesbury Sandstone, a tough resistant rock, capped by the Boyne Hollow Cherts, an even more durable rock. These layers of the Upper Greensand have eroded away slowly compared to the surrounding softer rocks, and thus have been responsible for the dominant position of the Shaftesbury Plateau. To the west, Duncliffe Hill appears, its steep wooded slopes rising quite abruptly from the clay pastures of Blackmoor Vale. It represents a former westwards extension of the Shaftesbury Plateau. It is also capped by tough resistant rocks, similar to those that form the Shaftesbury Plateau, and these have been responsible for its survival as an erosion remnant. Springs cutting back into a much more extended version of the Shaftesbury Plateau, have gradually eroded back and eventually isolated the residual feature of Duncliffe Hill, which is a clear dominant landscape feature when seen from much of Blackmoor Vale, and the crest of the Chalk escarpment to the south and southwest. Water percolating down through the sandstone of Duncliffe Hill has rendered the underlying Gault Clay unstable, and this is responsible for the numerous landslips that occur around the foot of the hill. Some of these landslips are still quite active, particularly after spells of wet weather. They form quite prominent bulges or toes in the surrounding fields, producing a hummocky, ill-drained landscape.

The Sherborne Escarpments

In the far northwest of Dorset the landscape is dominated by a series of escarpments that run from northeast to southwest. Although they do not give rise to any dominating landscape feature, the close juxtaposition of the different bands of rocks gives rise to an appealing and interesting variety in the landscape both to the north and the south of Sherborne itself. To the northwest there is a belt of relatively low-lying land underlain by the Yeovil Sands that lie just within Dorset. These strikingly yellow rocks are very well exposed in the deep cutting on Babylon Hill that carries the A30 road from Sherborne to Yeovil. The Yeovil Sands are succeeded in the geological column by the Inferior Oolite, an orange-yellow limestone, which forms the marked escarpment that runs from Bradford Abbas to Corton Hill just over the border in Somerset. Small tributaries of the River Yeo have cut back into this escarpment to give it a sharply indented outline near Nether and Over Compton and again in the northeast near Sandford Orcas. The Inferior Oolite is widely used as a building stone, whose mellow colour has contributed much to the distinctive nature of Sherborne's buildings. The gentle dip-slope of the Inferior Oolite extends southeastwards to the valley of the infant Yeo, beyond which rises another stepped escarpment. In its lower part, this feature is formed of Fuller's Earth, stiffened by the Fuller's Earth Rock, but it is capped by the Forest Marble, and forms such prominent features as Lillington Hill and the wooded hills overlooking Sherborne Castle. Further to the southeast the broken outcrop of the Cornbrash, another thin limestone, forms the drier land on which the villages of Longburton and Alweston are built.

Duncliffe Hill

The Sherborne Escarpments

THE CHALKLANDS

Badbury Rings

Badbury Rings, with its pine-clad summit, rising from the enclosing ramparts of the Iron Age hill-fort, is a prominent feature when seen from the beech-lined road that runs from Wimborne to Blandford. From the gravel-capped hills around Pamphill, the landscape tends to open out as the Chalk outcrop, with its familiar rolling outlines, is reached to the northwest, with Badbury Rings rising as a prominent landmark in the area to the northeast of Shapwick. The rising ground of the Rings, capped by the hill-fort, is predominantly of interest as an archaeological site, but it also bears witness to a much earlier geological stage in the development of the landscape. Within the Chalk there are some bands that are much harder and resistant to erosion than others. One, the so-called Belemnite Chalk, is encountered

Badbury Rings

high up in the Chalk sequence, and outcrops on the surface in a belt running from Windmill Hill just over the Hampshire border near Martin southwestwards towards the Stour valley near Shapwick. Much of this Belemnite Chalk has now been eroded away, but it remains to form prominent relict features in the Chalk landscape of north east Dorset, notably at Pentridge Hill, and at Badbury Rings. Careful examination of the footpaths that lead to the summit of Badbury Rings will reveal the existence of rounded flint pebbles. These pebbles are evidence for the sea invading this area some 60 million years ago, after initial uplift and erosion of the Chalk, since they probably represent an ancient beach deposit. This deposit of pebbles was probably much more extensive since there are other patches preserved elsewhere in the local area at King Down Farm and near Kingston Lacy. Once the pebble deposit had been removed by erosion the underlying Chalk surface is revealed and this surface slopes steadily upwards from Badbury Rings towards the highest parts of the Chalk on Cranborne Chase.

Black Down

West of Dorchester, the open Chalk country rises relentlessly towards the wooded slopes that lead up to Black Down. The heather-clad plateau of Black Down, with its distinctive landmark of the Hardy Monument, is one of Dorset's most visible upland summits, readily identified from the Isle of Portland, Purbeck's Chalk ridge, Eggardon's hill-fort and the highest parts of the central Chalk country. Black Down, with its windswept expanses of heather and gorse, is different from many of the other Chalk summits in Dorset,

Black Down

because it carries a fairly thick capping of sands and gravels. These deposits have been worked in the past and disused pits now scar the open ground to the south of the Hardy Monument. The gravels contain mainly flints from the Chalk, chert from the Upper Greensand and a range of 'foreign' pebbles that seem to have originated in Cornwall. It would appear that the summit gravels were laid down by a river that flowed into area from the southwest of England some 40 million years ago. This river would have transported gravel from the far southwest, but would also have picked up the chert and flint pebbles from locations much nearer in East Devon and West Dorset. Apart from their intrinsic geological interest, the gravels also have an important effect on the landscape. Sands and gravels tend to give rise to an acid soil, and this encourages the growth of heather and gorse, rather than the wide range of grasses that are found on other uncultivated Chalk uplands. Water percolating downwards from the sands and gravels is usually acid, and has probably dissolved out the underlying Chalk in places to form steep-sided shake-holes, similar to the ones on Bronkham Hill to the east, and Culpepper's Dish, near Briantspuddle. The plantations of conifers that cover most of the approaches to the summit have changed their character somewhat, particularly on gloomy winter days. It is in this season, when the dead heather darkens the summit of Black Down, that its name is perhaps most appropriate.

Bronkham Hill

This elongated hill is best seen from the heights of Black Down to the west. It extends away to the southeast for nearly a mile before it merges with the spur of Corton Hill overlooking Friar Waddon. A casual glance at the feature from near Hardy Monument on Black Down will first show the Bronze Age barrows arranged like a series of pimples along its summit ridge. Once on Bronkham Hill itself, investigation of the features identified on the Ordnance Survey Map as 'shake holes', reveals a series of steep-sided hollows, on average about 25 feet (8 metres) wide. There are over 160 of these hollows on Bronkham Hill and its flanks. In the sides of the track that runs along Bronkham Hill, flint gravels are seen. These gravels and sands overlie the Chalk, which forms the mass of Bronkham Hill. The hollows are dolines, formed by the solution of the chalk, by downward percolating water, acidified by the heathy cover. Many of the dolines appear to have been formed in the period between the building of the Bronze Age barrows (approximately 4000 BP [before present]) and the construc-tion of a defensive dyke across the area in approximately 1600, since the course of the latter takes advantage of the position of some of the dolines. Some writers claim to have seen contemporary formation of the hollows, with one noting a hole a foot wide at the surface, leading to a large cave 20 feet (6 metres) in diameter and 20 feet (6 metres) deep: there is no evidence of such a feature today! Bronkham Hill has a unique place in the scenic heritage of Dorset, displaying not only such fine dolines, but also possessing the distinctive Bronze Age barrows.

Bulbarrow and Woolland Hills

Thomas Hardy wrote, in his poem *Wessex Heights* (1896):
There are some heights in Wessex, shaped as if by a kindly hand
For thinking, dreaming, dying on…
… Or else on homely Bulbarrow …
Where men have never cared to haunt, nor women have walked with me,
And ghosts then keep their distance; and I know some liberty.
Over a hundred years later Bulbarrow and neighbouring Woolland Hill still have some of the same sense of remote-ness and tranquillity, although Hardy may not have approved of the two wireless masts that now stand on the summit of Bulbarrow. At 900 feet (274 metres), Bulbarrow is the

Bronkham Hill

Bulbarrow Hill

highest point on the great Chalk escarpment that runs across Dorset from Melbury Hill in the northeast to the heights above Beaminster in the southwest. Bulbarrow and Woolland stand out as a well-marked promontory on the escarpment, extending further out towards the Vale of Blackmoor in the two great spurs of White Hill to the west and The Launch to the east. White Hill, in particular, is well defined between two faults on either side, that have brought up the Chalk to form this magnificent protrusion of the escarpment to the north. Bulbarrow and Woolland owe much of their prominence to the work of scarp-foot springs in the Gault Clay that have eroded great combes in the escarpment in Balmers Coombe Bottom and the unnamed combe beneath Woolland Hill itself. The summit area that carries the wireless masts has been further isolated by the once-eroding valley heads to the south in Delcombe Head and under Cuckoo Lane Wood.

The Cliff, Blandford

The tree-covered slopes of The Cliff rise steeply from the western banks of the River Stour as it flows past the outskirts of Blandford. It is perhaps best appreciated on a day of high summer, when the rich greens and coppers of the beech foliage on The Cliff contrast with the slow flowing Stour with its cover of water-lilies and other aquatic plants. There is an abrupt contrast between the steep slopes of The Cliff and the flood-prone water meadows that lie on the opposite bank of the Stour. This difference between the two banks is explained by the way in which rivers flow. Most rivers flow in graceful curves or meanders at some stage in their course, simply because this is the most hydraulically efficient way for them to flow. The main current in a meander tends to be concentrated towards the outside of the bend, and it is here that the erosive power of the river is greatest. On the inside of the meander energy levels within the river are much less and deposition of silt and mud readily takes place there. With erosive power

The Cliff, Blandford

greatest on the outside of the bend the river cuts into its banks there, and eventually a steep feature known as a river cliff will develop. In some cases the river cliff may become unstable, and even collapse from time to time, but the well-rooted trees of The Cliff at Blandford bring a measure of stability to the steep slopes. A well-meandering river, such as the Stour will cut a whole sequence of river cliffs as it flows. Upstream from The Cliff, the Stour has cut another river cliff just to the north of Bryanston School and yet another on the western flanks of Hod Hill. River cliffs such as these often carry an attractive woodland cover, such as The Hanging below Bryanston, and Hod Wood on the flanks of Hod Hill. Downstream, Spetisbury is perched above yet another river cliff cut by the Stour, and similar features can be seen much lower down the river at Blackwater near Hurn, and at Sheepwash near Iford Bridge.

Compton Valence

Compton Valence is a small hamlet nestling in a hollow in the Chalk downland some 8 miles (13km) to the west of Dorchester. Geologically speaking, Compton Valence occupies the centre of a small dome or upfold in the rocks, similar

Compton Valence

to the much larger Vale of Marshwood structure in West Dorset. Doming of rocks essentially weakens the structure, and thus renders it more susceptible to erosion. Rain and small streams have opened up the Compton Valence structure to produce a hollow in the downland, revealing the rocks beneath the Chalk. As the streams have cut down, they have exposed successively older rocks, which outcrop in a series of concentric rings within the Chalk-rimmed lowland. In the lowest parts of this eroded hollow in the Chalk, the Fuller's Earth Clay is exposed. Around this Jurassic clay in the valley bottom, there is a marked bench formed by the tough Eggardon Grit, part of the Upper Greensand, which lies immediately beneath the Chalk cover. The sandstone church, overlooking the heart of the lowland, stands on a well-marked segment of this bench, as does the Rectory just to the west. Tout Hill, a prominent feature overlooking the hamlet from the south, is also formed of the Eggardon Grit. Here in the almost miniature Compton Valence lowland, there is a classic example of what geologists call *inverted relief*, where an upfold in the rocks has led to the Cretaceous cover being removed to reveal a window exposing the older Jurassic rocks beneath.

Dogbury Hill

Dogbury Hill lies on the Chalk escarpment in West Dorset, just to the east of the point where the Dorchester-Sherborne road slips through the gap in the scarp slope at Dogbury Gate. It owes its prominence to the manner in which the headwaters of two streams have cut back into the Chalk escarpment through headwardly eroding springs. To the west the headwaters of the Cerne River have cut back steadily to almost breach the escarpment at Dogbury Gate, leaving Dogbury Hill as a prominent feature overlooking Lyons Gate to the north. Two small tributaries of the River Stour, both flowing northwards, have cut back into the Chalk escarpment, increasing the dominance of Dogbury Hill. The River Cam has eroded back towards Dogbury Gate, and to the east the head-streams of the Caundle Brook have cut the huge combe in which Lyons Head Farm, with its several lakes, is situated. Dogbury Hill, although a significant feature of the Chalk escarpment, is essentially the northern bastion of the long Chalk ridge that extends southwards to Little Minterne Hill and Watts Hill. The Chalk at Dogbury Hill is underlain by the Upper Greensand and the Gault Clay. The latter is inherently unstable, and causes both the Upper Greensand and the Chalk to slip along the face of the escarpment.

Dogbury Hill

The Dorsetshire Gap

This break in the line of the Chalk escarpment that runs east-west across the middle of Dorset lies in the hidden and little frequented country to the west of Melcombe Bingham. It is not low enough to carry a north-south road across the escarpment, and is more in the nature of a high level col, with steep slopes both to the north and the south. It lies between the prominent feature of Nettlecombe Tout to the west and the smaller Nordon Hill to the east. Both of these features are formed of the higher layers of the Chalk, whereas the Dorsetshire Gap has seen erosion cutting down into the Lower Chalk. To the southeast of the Dorsetshire Gap is a broad embayment, floored by Upper Greensand, which leads down to the valley in which Cheselbourne is located. North of the Gap a tiny stream flows north through Melcombe Park to eventually join the River Lydden to the northwest of Hazelbury Bryan. This small brook is probably the clue to the formation of the Dorsetshire Gap. The spring in the Chalk that supports this stream is slowly cutting back into the Chalk escarpment and, as it does so, is eroding its way towards the Upper Greensand embayment on the other side of the escarpment. In this way, the col of the Dorsetshire Gap is slowly being lowered, and its steep sides will eventually become much more gentle.

Eggardon Hill

Rising to a height of 826 feet (252 metres) Eggardon Hill is the great bastion of the Chalk escarpment in West Dorset that dominates much of the country to the east of Bridport. From its summit, views extend westwards far along the coast into East Devon, and inland towards the heights of the Blackdown Hills. As is the case with so many of Dorset's outstanding Chalk hills an Iron Age fort crowns its summit. On the steep western faces of Eggardon there is a low rocky cliff feature that represents the outcrop of the tough Upper Greensand, known here as the Eggardon Grit. Eggardon throws out great billowing spurs of downland that extend northwards towards the Hooke valley, and southwards to Haydon Down and beyond to Askerswell Down. Much of this Chalkland, including Eggardon itself, carries a cover of flinty material, the result of a long continued period of erosion. Hummocky ground below Eggardon is evidence of the familiar landslides that develop where Chalk and Upper Greensand overlie the unstable Gault Clay below.

The Dorsetshire Gap

Eggardon Hill

Hambledon Hill

Hambledon Hill lies in the angle where the Chalk escarpment of North Dorset swings round from its north-south trend to its east-west alignment that carries it westwards to the Somerset boundary. With its neighbour, Hod Hill, Hambledon Hill is separated from the main escarpment by the valley of the River Stour to the west and the valley cut by its much smaller tributary, the Iwerne stream, to the east. Both hills are formed of the middle and upper beds of the Chalk, and rest on a platform of the lowest part of the Chalk, and the underlying Upper Greensand. The down-cutting of the Stour and the Iwerne stream have separated Hambledon Hill from the main escarpment, and it owes much of its prominence to its isolated position. Both the east and west faces of Hambledon Hill are broken by well developed combes, which were probably initiated by spring action, and enlarged by erosion around large patches of snow in the Ice Age. The two eastern arms of Hambledon Hill enclose Coombe Bottom, now a dry valley, cut by a small tributary of the Iwerne stream when the level of water in the Chalk was higher. A prominent hill fort adds distinctive character to the summit of Hambledon.

The High Valleys of Cranborne Chase

Around Dorset's highest village, Ashmore, a series of deep valleys cut into the open Chalk country of Cranborne Chase. They are particularly well displayed to the east of the high road from Blandford to Shaftesbury, just before it begins its precipitous descent of Spreadeagle Hill into Melbury Abbas. These high valleys once fed tributaries into two of Dorset's most beautiful chalk watercourses, the Tarrant and the Gussage streams. All of the Cranborne Chase valleys are now dry, although after an exceptionally wet winter a stream may flow temporarily in the valley bottoms, particularly towards their lower ends. The depth of these valleys is eloquent testimony to the erosive power of water at some time in the past, most probably during the Ice Age. Various theories have been put forward to explain the existence of these deeply cut dry valleys. Some writers suggest that during the Ice Age all of the water within the pore spaces of the Chalk would have been frozen, thus rendering it impermeable to the downward passage of water. This would have encouraged surface flow of water, particularly when the spring thaw released large volumes of water from the snow-fields that would have covered Cranborne Chase at that time.

Hambledon Hill

The High Valleys of Cranborne Chase

Others consider that, as the great Chalk escarpment that runs from Shaftesbury southwards and westwards through Dorset retreated, the level of water (the water table) in the Chalk would have fallen, thus drying out the high valleys.

Longcombe Bottom

Longcombe Bottom is the best developed of a series of dry valleys that dissect the great Chalk escarpment that runs north-south from Melbury Hill to Hambledon Hill overlooking the River Stour. It runs northeastwards from the village of Fontmell Magna, effectively separating the great spur of Fontmell Down from a similar spur to the south that carries the minor road from Sutton Clump to the village of Sutton Waldron. All of these valleys have been cut by streams that have their origin in springs that issued at the foot of the Chalk escarpment. Rainwater drains down through the permeable Chalk and the underlying Cann Sand of the Upper Greensand, which is also permeable, until it reaches the Gault Clay below. Since the Gault is impermeable, the percolating water feeds a series of springs which mark the junction of the rocks of varying permeability. As these springs develop they tend to erode headwards, gradually

producing a steep-sided valley in the Chalk escarpment. When the water table in the Chalk was much higher than at present, the well-nourished springs would have cut valleys such as Longcombe Bottom that extends back some 1½ miles (800 metres) into the escarpment. With a falling water table, perhaps related to the retreat of the escarpment itself, the valleys would begin to dry out, and the springs would retreat down valley. Today, Longcombe Bottom is only occupied by a stream, Collyers Brook, in its lower reaches.

Lyscombe Bottom

Lyscombe Bottom is a huge embayment in the Chalk downland immediately south of the escarpment at Nettlecombe Tout. It occupies an area of almost ⅓ square mile (square kilometre), and is bounded on the west by the steep slopes of Lyscombe Hill, and on the east by the equally steep declivities of Bowdens and Hog Hill. What makes Lyscombe Bottom a quite remarkable landscape feature is the very narrow exit to the south, just to the north of Lyscombe Farm, like the constraining neck of a bottle. It is here that the tiny Lyscombe stream rises and flows southwards to join the River Piddle just to the northwest of Puddletown.

Longcombe Bottom

Lyscombe Bottom

An examination of the geological map of the area will show that Lyscombe Bottom is floored with Lower Chalk, and the steep confining slopes are cut in the Middle Chalk. The high narrow ridge separating Lyscombe Bottom from the Folly lowland to the northwest is formed of the tougher Upper Chalk. It would seem that the unusual shape of Lyscombe Bottom may well have resulted from the powerful work of a stream that was eroding headwards. Once it had broken through the Upper and Middle Chalk around Lyscombe Farm it would have revealed the less resistant beds of the Lower Chalk, and was able to open up the sizeable embayment that we see today. A falling water table would have caused the spring to retreat southwards to its present position near Lyscombe Farm.

Melbury Hill

Melbury Hill is the most northeasterly outpost of the great Chalk escarpment that sweeps across Dorset from Winyard's Gap to Charlton Down and Win Green in Wiltshire. At 863 feet (263 metres) it is exceeded in height on the escarpment only by Bulbarrow Hill, and by the high crest that runs from Telegraph Hill to Gore Hill above Hilfield. It stands out as a bastion of the escarpment, isolated to the north by the

incised valley of the Cann stream, and to the south by the deep combe that separates it from Fontmell Down. Its summit is capped by the highest beds of the Chalk, and it is linked to the main escarpment by the narrow Compton Down. Much of this high Chalk downland of North Dorset remained unsubmerged when the sea swept over most of Dorset 5 million years ago. Thus the smooth slopes of Melbury Hill represent landforms that have been sculpted by rain and run-off for nearly 50 million years.

Pentridge Hill

Pentridge Hill is seen to the southeast of the Blandford to Salisbury Road as a long whaleback-shaped feature, rising beyond the half-hidden village of Pentridge. Standing above the gently rolling Chalk downlands of north east Dorset, it is formed by a harder, more resistant band in the Chalk, which also forms Windmill Hill in Hampshire just to the east, and the more distant Gallows Hill in Wiltshire. Penbury Knoll 606 feet (184 metres), with its thicket of pines, is the highest point of Pentridge Hill. The deep combes of either side were probably formed in the Ice Age, when they would have been filled with snow for much of the year; freezing and thawing around these patches of snow would have

Melbury Hill

Pentridge Hill

enlarged the Ice Age hollows to their present size. In the fields just to the east of Penbury Knoll there are numerous small, rounded flint pebbles which indicate that the highest parts of Pentridge Hill carry an isolated capping of much younger rocks than the Chalk, the Reading Beds. These pebbly sands appear at the surface in a more continuous belt to the southeast between Fordingbridge and Horton.

The Sydling – Cerne Chalk Downlands

To many people a typical Dorset landscape would embrace sweeping Chalk downland dissected by deep valleys, with clear streams flowing through the water meadows along their floors. Much of Dorset is occupied by the great swathe of Chalkland that runs across the County from Cranborne Chase in the northeast to the high open country to the west of Dorchester. The central block of downland, drained by the two Chalk streams of Sydling Water and the Cerne River, displays the essential character of Dorset's Chalk landscapes. From the high crest of the bounding Chalk escarpment to the north, which reaches heights of over 850 feet (259 metres) at High Stoy Hill and Gore Hill, the downlands of the Chalk dip slope extend down to the terrace-fringed valley of the Frome to the south. To the southeast, younger Tertiary rocks floor the downfold of the Frome syncline. The highest parts of the downland in the north may represent a very ancient surface cut by rain and rivers many millions of years ago. Lower down the crest of the downland hills may still carry the remnants of a marine-cut plain that is more recent in origin, but evidence for this surface is still largely conjectural. Remnants of Tertiary Beds on the higher summits to the southeast of Godmanstone suggest that the lowest parts of the dip slope may have been exhumed from beneath a more extensive Tertiary cover. It is thus possible that this block of downland has undergone several phases of landscape evolution, including the periglacial modification of the older Tertiary slopes during the colder climate of the Ice Age. The thick deposits of Clay-with-Flints that mantle the upper surfaces of the dip slope pose interest-

The Sydling – Cerne Chalk Downlands

ing problems too; are they the result of tropical weathering in Tertiary times or are they reworked products of wind deposition, or frost shattering in the Ice Age?

The Valley of Stones

Cutting into the high Chalk downland to the west of Hardy Monument is the Valley of Stones. The dry valley heads near the road that crosses the downs from Portesham Hill crossroads to Abbotsbury, and then curves northwestwards towards Little Bredy Farm. In its upper reaches, the floor of the valley is littered with blocks of tough, indurated sandstone known as grey wethers (for their resemblance to a flock of sheep), or, more commonly, as sarsen stones. They are not uncommon in other upland Chalk valleys, and are well displayed in the valleys of the Marlborough Downs in Wiltshire. They appear to be the remnants of hard crusts that developed in the sandy formations that covered the Chalk of the West Dorset Downs at one time. It is thought that these crusts developed from the deposition of silica from downward percolating solutions, probably when the climate was much warmer. The blocks have reached their present position in the valley bottom by slow downward movement during the Ice Age, when valley sides became unstable during the brief period of thawing in the summer. Sarsen stones were used in prehistoric times for

The Valley of Stones

building such features as the Grey Mare and her Colts, a long barrow on the Chalk upland a few hundred yards to the west of the Valley of Stones.

Winyard's Gap

Winyard's Gap is one of the last bastions of the Chalk uplands in West Dorset. It is approached along the long stretch of road from Maiden Newton that runs along the crest of the Chalk downland. Along this road there are expansive views of Dorset's western Chalklands, but at Winyard's Gap there is a dramatic change of scene, with much of the lower and infinitely varied Jurassic country of southern Somerset around Crewkerne coming into view as the Dorset uplands are left behind. The Gap represents a break in the Chalk escarpment between the slightly higher land to the north extending towards Crook Hill, and similar heights just behind the village of Chedington. The lower land in Winyard's Gap is

probably the work of springs eating back into the Chalk from two directions. To the west the headwaters of Somerset's River Parrett have eroded back into the Chalk escarpment to produce a deep amphitheatre in the relatively soft Fuller's Earth. On the eastern side, the streams that eventually drain down towards Halstock and the Sutton Bingham Reservoir have also cut back into the Chalk in a series of steep-sided valleys. The combined effect of the two sets of streams eroding back has been to gradually lower the land around Winyard's Gap itself, producing a col in the Chalk escarpment. Beneath the Chalk at Winyard's Gap is the Upper Greensand, which rests in turn on the Gault Clay. The junction between the two latter rocks is, as elsewhere in Dorset, an unstable one, and this has resulted in much landslipping immediately below Winyard's Gap, producing a hummocky landscape at the foot of the escarpment and creating problems for highway maintenance as the Maiden Newton–Crewkerne road descends the escarpment.

Winyard's Gap

EAST DORSET

Beacon Hill

Beacon Hill is one of the most familiar landmarks on the western outskirts of Broadstone. Its distinct wooded outline is clearly seen from the high plateau around Tower Park, and its profile can be easily recognised from the Purbeck Hills to the south. It is formed of sands that belong to the Poole formation, laid down some 35 to 40 million years ago, probably on the edge of a sea in the area that was open to the east. Erosion of these sands has given rise to its almost conical shaped profile. This is in marked contrast to much of the flat topped scenery in the area to the immediate east, as on Canford Heath, where river terrace gravels produce a completely different profile. Beacon Hill stands out from a landscape that has suffered from the working of both sand and clay from the Poole Formation in a series of pits that

Beacon Hill

extend from Henbury in the north to the nearby Beacon Hill pit.

The Bournemouth Chines

The Bournemouth Chines are a series of deeply-notched valleys that cut into the cliffs over several miles from Flaghead Chine, a mile east of Sandbanks to Honeycombe Chine, just to the east of Boscombe Pier. The largest of this sequence of valleys is the Bourne, much longer than the others and bearing all the evidence of a complicated evolution. All of the smaller chines are steep-sided and for the most part wooded, and have thus resisted the spread of Bournemouth and Poole's urban sprawl across the enclosing gravel plateaux that constitute the site on which much of the conurbation is built. Valley profiles within the chines vary a great deal. In the longer chines such as Branksome Chine and Boscombe Chine, there appears to be an outer valley, which has a broadly U-shaped profile in cross-section, into which a much more steep-sided inner valley has been cut nearer the coast. The outer valley appears to be poorly represented in the shorter chines such as Durley Chine and Alum Chine, only appearing at their heads some way inland from the coast, with most of the valley displaying a steep-sided cross profile. The explanation of the form of these chines lies in the interpretation of coastal change in the very recent geological past. Between 5000 and 10,000 years ago, when the sea made its erosional entry into the old Solent River valley, which ran west-east across the present Poole Bay, cliffs began to develop along the northern edge of the new embayment.

Brownsea Island

Alum Chine

The long, low, flat-topped profile of Brownsea Island is a familiar sight to all who use Poole Harbour, or who live on its shores. In common with the other four islands in Poole Harbour, it owes its origin to the post-glacial rise in sea level during which the lower part of the present Frome valley, then part of the much larger Solent River valley, was flooded. Only the highest parts of this stretch of the Solent River valley, such as the gravel-capped Brownsea Island, survived this flooding. Most of Brownsea is built of Tertiary sediments, which were laid down by a large river, which flowed into the area from the west some forty million years ago. The sediments consist of two layers, the lower Parkstone Clay, and the overlying Branksome Sands. Both of these layers are well exposed on the western and northern shores of the island, although they are particularly subject to erosion, and there are numerous cliff falls. St Andrew's Bay, on the eastern side of the island was enclosed in the middle of the nine-

Brownsea Island

Erosion of these cliffs was so rapid that the streams draining the chines were forced to cut down rapidly to adjust to the encroaching sea. Thus an inner valley began to be incised into the broader more open outer valley. In the shorter chines this adjustment is almost complete, with much of the older broader valley having been eroded away. In the larger chines the two-phase evolution is still clearly visible.

teenth century, and the reclaimed pastures were kept drained by a windmill. In the 1930s, however, the area was allowed to become flooded again and today it is a non-tidal lagoon of brackish water, mudflats and reeds, which is part of the Wildlife Sanctuary and Wildlife Reserve. The clays within the Tertiary sediments were exploited for the production of copperas in the sixteenth and seventeenth centuries, and for the manufacture of ceramic ware in the eighteenth and nineteenth centuries. Copperas was used as a colour fixer in the dyeing industry, for tanning and in the manufacture of inks and pigments. Brownsea clays are not of the highest quality, and only terracotta products and coarse pottery were produced, the broken fragments of which can be seen along the north-western shore of the island.

Culpepper's Dish

Just ½ mile (800 metres) south of the village of Briantspuddle, opposite a picnic site, Culpepper's Dish is one of Dorset's most unusual landscape features. It is the largest of a series of roughly circular hollows that occur on the now forested heaths between Higher Bockhampton and Briantspuddle. Culpepper's Dish measures some 280 feet (85 metres) in diameter and has a depth of approximately 70 feet (21 metres). Shaped like an inverted cone, it is now partly obscured by the growth of oak/birch scrub and young Scots pines on its steep slopes. In this area, layers of gravels and sands overlie the Chalk. Soils that have developed on the gravels support acidic heathland vegetation, so slightly acid water percolates downwards through the sands into the Chalk below, slowly dissolving it. The overlying sands and gravels are left unsupported and collapse into cavities left by the solution of the Chalk. Although the process has been operative for thousands of years, it is still active today. The pines planted in the area have encouraged even more acid groundwater to develop, increasing the rate of solution of the Chalk.

Culpepper's Dish

Gallows Hill

This prominent hill lies some 3 miles south of Bere Regis just to the east of the point where the road from Bere Regis to Wool reaches its highest point before the long descent into the Frome Valley at Wool. Its name clearly needs no

Gallows Hill

gravel caps a prominent point such as Gallows Hill, a distinctive landscape feature results. Today its dominance has been much modified by afforestation, but its name serves to remind us of a grisly past.

St Catherine's Hill

Lying between the rivers Stour and Avon just to the north of Christchurch, the wooded feature of St Catherine's Hill dominates the lower valleys of both rivers before they join and flow into Christchurch Harbour. St Catherine's Hill is more of a plateau than a hill, and owes its flat-topped nature to a capping of river gravels. These gravels were laid down by the Avon and Stour nearly two million years ago, when both rivers flowed at a much higher level. With the onset of the Ice Age, sea levels were lowered because water was abstracted to form the ice sheets. As the sea level fell, rivers such as the Stour and Avon began to cut down into their valleys, leaving their old floodplain gravels at their higher level and forming river terraces. St Catherine's Hill is one of the highest terraces in the lower valleys of the Stour and the Avon. Its pine-covered slopes fall steeply down to the water meadows of the Avon to the east, and to the eastward

explanation, and the isolated hill, standing out from the sombre heathlands to the east and west would no doubt have been an ideal site for the location of a gibbet. Much of the land between the Piddle Valley to the north and the Frome Valley to the south in this part of eastern Dorset is underlain by the sands and clays of the Poole Formation. These beds promote the development of acid soils, which readily encourage the growth of heathland, and before the current phase of afforestation, the heaths surrounding Gallows Hill, such as Wool Heath to the south, and Bere Heath to the north would have been typical expanses of Hardy's beloved Egdon Heath. It is likely that in the Ice Age, when Dorset experienced a periglacial or tundra-like climate, both the Piddle and the Frome would have carried a great deal of meltwater in the summer and would have wandered across the area that now separates the two rivers, depositing thick spreads of gravel to form what are today high-level river terraces. Much of the gravel has been removed by subsequent erosion, and today the sheets of gravel are confined to the highest land between the two rivers. Over large areas, on either side of the road from Worgret to the crossroads south of Gallows Hill, the gravel and underlying sand are worked for use in the construction industry. Where the

St Catherine's Hill

sweep of the meandering Stour to the west. Eastwards a 'staircase' of terraces rises steadily upwards to the distant skyline of the New Forest.

Stanpit Marshes

Stanpit and Grimbury Marshes form one of the largest extents of salt marsh to be found in Dorset. They occupy an area between the main channel in Christchurch Harbour and the small, now suburbanised, village of Stanpit to the east. After Christchurch Harbour was formed as a result of the drowning of the lower parts of the Stour and Avon valleys in the post–glacial sea level rise, the rivers began to deposit sediment in the shallow waters of the estuary. As the sediment built up, small channels and creeks began to develop, thus isolating areas of mud, which were gradually colonised by plants that can tolerate relatively high levels of salinity. Tidal movements were gradually slowed down by the plants, mainly the glassworts in the first instance, but later both sea purslane and seablite also appeared. Gradually the mud banks built up around the colonising plants, and the marsh emerged above high tide level. Stanpit Marsh is probably the oldest and earliest colonised part of the marshes. Mother Siller's Channel effectively separates Stanpit Marsh from the more recently formed Grimbury Marsh and at one time it extended inwards to the *Ship in Distress* pub on the main road from Christchurch to Mudeford. Gradually the creeks became narrower as sediment built up. The most recent accumulation of marsh is Blackberry Island to the southeast of the main marsh; it has now emerged above high water mark. The innermost parts of the marshes have now been drained so that they can support grazing animals. Crouch Hill is the highest place on the marshes and rises to all of 15 feet (4 metres) above sea level. There is some

Stanpit Marshes

evidence of marsh edge erosion at present, and careful moni-toring of developments will be needed if the marshes are to survive in their present form.

Woodbury and Black Hills, Bere Regis

Bere Regis lies within the shallow valley of the Bere stream that drains a considerable area of Chalk country to the north and northwest of the village. Rising to both the west and the east of the valley of the Bere stream are the well wooded heights of Black Hill and Woodbury Hill. Both of these hills are part of the intermittent escarpment formed by the lowest members of the Tertiary Beds that overlie the Chalk in the centre of the downfold in the rocks of central Dorset, known as the Frome syncline. Normally the lowest Tertiary

Beds are not particularly tough, but pebble beds do stiffen up the Tertiaries to make them more resistant to erosion, and thus form an escarpment to mark the junction with the underlying Chalk. Capping both Black Hill and Woodbury Hill there are deposits of Plateau gravel, probably laid down by the River Piddle and its tributaries when they were flowing at a much higher level in the period immediately before the Ice Age. Gravel deposits such as these have a protective function, and thus prevent erosion of the rocks immediately below, further emphasising the way in which Black Hill and Woodbury Hill dominate the valley of the Bere stream as it passes from the Chalk outcrop on to the Tertiaries. Woodbury Hill carries an Iron Age hill-fort on its summit; Black Hill, equally dominant in the landscape, can boast no more than a few scattered tumuli and a gravel pit.

Woodbury Hill

Black Hill

WEST DORSET

Abbotsbury Castle

This hill occupies one of the most prominent positions in West Dorset. From its commanding heights, extensive views open up over all of the Bride Valley, and all of the coast as far west as Lyme Regis. It lies at the western end of a long ridge that runs westwards from White Hill to the north of Abbotsbury. White Hill itself is made of Chalk, but the ridge to the west is made up of Upper Greensand. This ridge owes some of its steep-sided character to the erosive action of springs along its northern flanks. The little streams which originate from these springs eventually flow into the River Bride, which reaches the sea farther to the west at Freshwater. From Abbotsbury Castle, which is crowned by a triangular hill fort, there is a long and steady slope down to the sea and Chesil Beach. This slope is cut in the Forest

Marble and the Fuller's Earth, much older rocks of middle Jurassic Age. The Upper Greensand is underlain by the unstable Gault Clay, and this had led to the usual extensive landslipping, which is particularly well marked on the northern side of the road from Abbotsbury to Swyre. Landslipping is also evident on the long slopes that lead down to Ashley Chase House on the northern side of Abbotsbury Castle.

The Bridport Hills

The West Dorset town of Bridport is set in an attractive landscape drained by the River Brit and its main tributary, the Mangerton River. The road out of Bridport to the west has to climb steeply over the sandy ridges to Chideock. Similarly the Dorchester road has to surmount the barrier of

Abbotsbury Castle

The Bridport Hills: Colmer's Hill, west of Bridport

the limestone hills to the east of Walditch, before beginning the long climb to the Chalk uplands of Askerswell Down. It is, however, in the immediate vicinity of Bridport that lower hills present much of geological interest. Perhaps the most distinctive of Bridport's hills is the conical Colmer's Hill, with its cluster of pines on its summit. It is formed of the Bridport Sands, the bright yellow sandstones that are exposed in West Bay's East Cliff. Nearer to Bridport is the more flat-topped Allington Hill, capped this time by tough Inferior Oolite Limestones. On the other side of the valley of the Brit, Bridport's older residences clamber up the sides

of Coneygar Hill, again formed of yellow sandstone. Just to the north the outlying steep-sided Watton Hill bears another remnant of Oolitic Limestone on its summit. Few country market towns can lay claim to so much geological variety within their bounds.

Chapel Hill

St Catherine's Chapel, set in its splendidly isolated position on the summit of Chapel Hill, Abbotsbury, is one of the most familiar landmarks in West Dorset. Chapel Hill is one

Chapel Hill

of a series of east-west aligned hills formed from the Corallian Beds, which extend as far east as the coast just to the east of Bowleaze Cove beyond Weymouth. The hills are a prominent feature of the landforms that have been eroded from the rocks of the Weymouth anticline, an important upfold of Middle and Upper Jurassic rocks in south central Dorset. Resistant rocks such as the sands and grits of the Corallian Beds form lines of hills in the Weymouth anticline, such as those noted above, and also the high ground on which Wyke Regis is built. Softer rocks, such as the Oxford Clay form parallel low-lying vales, such as the land around Rodden, and the valley running west from just south of Broadwey. In the northern line of Corallian hills the beds are dipping northwards, and, when eroded, form escarpments, landscape features that have a steep facing southern slope, the scarp slope, and a more gentle northern slope, the dip slope. The contrasting slopes are well seen on Chapel Hill, which owes its isolation to the erosive work of two tiny streams on either side. Seen from the summit of Abbotsbury Hill, erosion has produced in Chapel Hill an almost flat-iron profile, repeated in the hills to the immediate east and west. The soil on the northern approaches to the summit of Chapel Hill is a reddish-brown colour, which results from a thin covering of the so-called Abbotsbury Iron Ore. This iron ore is well exposed in the lanes to the north of Abbotsbury, but it has never been worked because of its high silica content. Human activity has punctuated the profile of Chapel Hill with a series of well-marked strip lynchets, or cultivation terraces, probably of medieval origin.

The Knoll

Overlooking the village of Puncknowle on one side and the main road from Abbotsbury to Burton Bradstock on the other, the Knoll is one of West Dorset's most attractive smaller landscape features. It is best seen from the summit of Limekiln Hill to the southeast and dominates much of the country from there to Burton Bradstock.

The Knoll

The Knoll is essentially an Upper Greensand hill, similar to the much larger outlier hills away to the northwest near to the Devon border such as Lambert's Castle Hill and Coney's Castle. Much of the lower country around the Knoll is underlain by the Forest Marble or the Cornbrash, both of Middle Jurassic age. Smooth slopes rise up from the Forest Marble country to the summit of the Knoll and are everywhere mantled by periglacial debris that accumulated during the Ice Age. At one time, perhaps over a million years ago, the Knoll was already established as a well-marked landscape feature. During the very cold winters much of the surface layers would have frozen, and then during the brief spring melting would have occurred, causing the superficial material on the slopes to move downwards in a process known as solifluction. As it moved downwards it would have spread out to form an apron of debris on the country below. Some of this debris still remains on the summit, with the bare Greensand slopes appearing on every side. On the northwest there is a small landslipped area, which also probably originated in periglacial times. The Knoll's most distinctive features are the small ruined cottage on the summit, once used by coastguards, and the patch of dark conifers on its northern slopes. Both combine to make a unique presence in the coastal landscape of West Dorset.

Pilsdon Pen

The prominent hill of Pilsdon Pen lies in West Dorset, its distinctive angular profile dominating the Axe Valley in Devon to the north and Marshwood Vale in Dorset to the south. At 908 feet (277 metres), Pilsdon Pen is traditionally Dorset's highest point, and on a fine day the Mendips, the Quantocks and the Blackdown Hills can be seen from its summit. It owes its dominance to its geology. Together with its wooded neighbour, Lewesdon Hill (which is now thought to be several feet higher), Pilsdon Pen is formed of Upper Greensand, a tough durable rock some 100 million years old. The Greensand is strengthened towards the summit by bands of chert siliceous material, which is even more resistant to erosion. Fragments of both the greenish-grey Upper Greensand and the buff coloured chert can be found on the track leading up to the summit and its Iron Age hill-fort. The cover of Upper Greensand in West Dorset was formerly much more extensive, but erosion has removed it from all but the highest summits at Lewesdon, Pilsdon Pen, and Lambert's Castle Hill to the southwest.

Pilsdon Pen

Seaborough Hill

Seaborough is another of Dorset's frontier hills, with the county boundary with Somerset running along its crest. This Chalk and Greensand hill overlooks Crewkerne to the north and has become physically isolated by the headwaters of the Axe Valley to the south. It is in this area of northwest Dorset that the great Chalk escarpment that can be traced right across Dorset begins to break down into a series of isolated remnants. To the west of Winyard's Gap the escarpment decreases in height and Mosterton Down and Seaborough Hill are the two most westerly outliers of the Chalk in Dorset. In the far northwest of Dorset there is a battleground between the headwaters of the Somerset Parrett and the Devon Axe. As these streams compete for territory, the effect has been to isolate the western remnants of the Chalk escarpment from one another. Thus a tributary of the Axe is cutting north between Seaborough and Mosterton Down, and a tributary of the Parrett is cutting south producing the low gap floored by Fuller's Earth that separates the two hills. On the southern slopes of Seaborough Hill there is a series of landslips, once again the result of the instability of the underlying Gault Clay.

Seaborough Hill

Shipton Hill

The distinctive profile of Shipton Hill dominates much of the pleasant rolling country to the east of Bridport. Its up-turned boat shape can be particularly well noticed when seen end-on from the high stretch of the A35 just to the west of Askerswell. It displays an equally prominent role in the landscape when seen from the coast road from Swyre to Burton Bradstock. Shipton Hill is formed of Upper Greensand, resting on a bench of older Jurassic rocks, although landslipped material surrounds much of the feature. It is one of a series of Upper Greensand hills that are important elements in the scenery in this part of West Dorset. Others include Hammiton Hill, just to the south of Shipton Hill, and, farther away to the southeast, the Knoll near Swyre, with its abandoned coastguard's cottage on the summit. All three are western outriders of the much more extensive cover of Upper Greensand and Chalk that form the high downland to the east. Erosion has removed much of this cover to the west, leaving only these hill remnants to form the commanding heights of the landscape.

Shipton Hill

The Vale of Marshwood

The lowland of the Vale of Marshwood is one of West Dorset's most valued landscapes. It is perhaps best seen from the southern slopes of Pilsdon Pen, the dominant Greensand summit that overlooks it from the north. From here it appears as a great bowl, surrounded on every side by the angular hills so characteristic of West Dorset. On the west it is overshadowed by Lambert's Castle Hill, and Coney's Castle. It is separated from the waters of Lyme Bay by the broken line of Greensand hills that run from Stonebarrow through Hardown Hill to the isolated summit of Denhay Hill. Its eastern margins are formed by the more open rolling country developed on the sandy beds of the Lower Jurassic rocks. The Vale of Marshwood itself is underlain by easily eroded shales and marls, which give rise to the rich pastures and damp coppices that give the lowland its intimate appeal. It appears to have been formed as a result of the broad updoming of the Jurassic rocks in West Dorset.

This updoming weakened the rock sequence, allowing the upper sandy beds to be eroded away, revealing the shales and marls, which are much more vulnerable to erosion.

The Vale of Marshwood

SOUTH DORSET

Chalbury Hill

Chalbury Hill is the high feature that dominates the Sutton Poyntz lowland from the west. The lowland is surrounded by a series of hills, mostly Chalk on the north, but on the south and west the enclosing higher ground is of Portland Sand and Portland Stone. These Upper Jurassic rocks to the south and west of Sutton Poyntz have been brought to the surface by the uparching of rocks in the Weymouth anticline and its subsidiary minor upfold which runs through Sutton Poyntz. The Portland Stone, in particular, is much more resistant to erosion than the Kimmeridge Clay exposed in the core of the Sutton Poyntz upfold and to the south in the corridor that runs from Preston towards Littlemoor. There is a small patch of Purbeck Beds capping the Portland Stone that forms the main mass of Chalbury Hill, and a much

Chalbury Hill

larger remnant of these beds is found on the higher ground to the west of Coombe Valley. Chalbury Hill tends to be emphasised by this deep valley to the west, which itself appears to have had an interesting evolutionary history. It originates to the north of Chalbury Hill in a steep-sided combe in the Chalk and then runs south to isolate Chalbury Hill to the east and finally cuts its way through the ridge formed by the Corallian rocks at Jordan Hill to enter the ill-drained ground to the east of Lodmoor. Its course intersects the principal structural line of the main Sutton Poyntz upfold, a drainage anomaly which suggests that it originated on an ancient sea floor which cut right across the area several million years ago.

Friar Waddon and Corton Hills

Both Friar Waddon and Corton Hills are narrow steep-sided hogback features that mark the northern fringe of the Weymouth lowland. They are the most prominent members of a line of hills that run eastwards from the little hamlet of Waddon to Upwey. The Weymouth lowland has been eroded from a series of Middle and Upper Jurassic rocks that have been deformed to create the upfold of the Weymouth anticline. Since the main forces responsible for this folding of the Jurassic rocks were operating from the south, the fold is an asymmetrical one, with a gently dipping limb on the south (in the Isle of Portland) and a much more steeply dipping limb in the north. Where the dips are steep the surface outcrop of the rocks is necessarily narrow. If the rocks are reasonably resistant to erosion, narrow outcrops will give rise to quite steep-sided or hogback hills (the

Friar Waddon and Corton Hills

The Sutton Poyntz Lowland

The village of Sutton Poyntz lies within a small lowland about 4 miles (6½km) to the northeast of Weymouth. The lowland is about 2 miles (3km) from east to west and little more than ½ mile (800 metres) from north to south. It is everywhere surrounded by hills, the only entrance being though the gap cut to the south by the little River Jordan, which enters the sea at Bowleaze Cove. To the north the lowland is bounded by the high Chalk escarpment of White Horse Hill, with its figure of George III on horseback, cut in the Chalk. To the south there is an irregular line of hills formed mainly of the Portland Sand and the Portland Limestone, with the occasional capping of Purbeck Beds as at Winslow. To the west the lowland is dominated by Chalbury, with its summit hill-fort built on another capping of Purbeck Beds. The Sutton Poyntz lowland has been excavated by erosion along an upfold of the Jurassic rocks. Upfolds always present a line of weakness to erosion, which has cut down through the overlying Chalk and Jurassic Limestones to reveal the Kimmeridge Clay, which outcrops in the lowland itself.

Hogsback in Surrey is the typical example). Both Friar Waddon and Corton Hills are formed of Portland Sand, with a capping of Portland Limestone. Within the Portland Sand there are bands of hard limestones, known as cementstones that are more resistant to erosion than the Kimmeridge Clay, which outcrops in the valley drained by the Pucksey Brook to the south. Thus the resistant Portland Limestone, together with the underlying Portland Sand, stiffened by the cementstones, form a narrow escarpment overlooking the lowland from the north. A narrow gap, cut by the small stream that drains south to the Pucksey Brook, separates the two hills, and a similar gap separates Corton Hill from the continuation of the ridge to the west. Both gaps were cut by streams that run north–south, against the geological structure. They would appear to have developed on an ancient marine plain, cut across the structure, and then maintained their courses as they cut downwards. Today's gaps, at right angles to the ridge, are a reminder of the past evolution of streams in the area. In both of these gaps the steeply dipping Portland Sand is exposed, providing one of the few easily accessible exposures of this formation in Dorset.

The Sutton Poyntz lowland

THE ISLE OF PURBECK

The Agglestone

Crowning an isolated hill in the heathlands some ½ mile (800 metres) to the northwest of Studland, the 20 feet (6 metres) high Agglestone, weighing some 500 tons, is made of tough indurated sandstone. It is best approached by a track that runs across Studland Heath from the Corfe Castle to Studland road. Along the track are scattered blocks of hard, dark brown rock, a sandstone, with small fragments of quartz included. It is this heathstone, as it is known locally, that has been widely used in the construction of walls, barns and cottages. The Agglestone is made of similar material, and it has survived because this sandstone is more resistant to erosion than the underlying gritty sands. Originally the Agglestone was anvil-shaped, being supported on a pedestal of slightly less tough sandstone. However in 1970 the Agglestone toppled over to one side, no doubt the result of underlying erosion. Its sandstone mass has protected the gorse-covered knoll on which it stands, prominent above the marshy valley bottoms on either side.

The Agglestone

The Cocknowle Gap

Cocknowle is the name of a small hamlet, some 3 miles (5km) to the west of Corfe Castle in Purbeck. Just to the west of the few cottages that make up this small settlement, the Cocknowle Gap is one of the most striking breaks in the Chalk ridge that runs from Worbarrow Bay to Handfast Point. At Cocknowle the Chalk ridge drops in height from nearly 500 feet (152 metres) on Knowle Hill to 370 feet (112 metres), rising again to over 600 feet (182 metres) on Ridgeway Hill. This gap or col probably marks the original passage of a small stream across the ridge at this point, a companion to those that now cross the ridge at Corfe Castle. What is remarkable about the Cocknowle Gap is that immediately north of the col there is a deep longitudinal valley cut in the Chalk. Its head is shallow and open, but it

The Cocknowle Gap

deepens steadily eastwards until it is over 150 feet (45 metres) deep, and then it turns suddenly northwards and leaves the Chalk ridge in a narrow gorge-like exit. This valley is evidently much younger than the high level col, and appears to have been cut during glacial times by summer meltwater rushing down a shallower valley cut in pre-glacial times. Its abrupt turn to the north is something of a mystery, possibly caused by a line of weakness in the Chalk. The relationship of the high level col to the younger valley is another puzzle, but the two features combine to give one of the most scenic crossings of the Purbeck Hills.

Corfe Castle

Corfe Castle, built on its steep-sided hill, occupies one of the most dramatic sites in Dorset. On either side of the hill, two small streams, the Corfe River and the Byle Brook, have cut gaps in the steeply-dipping Chalk of the Purbeck Hills. Single gaps cut by rivers through Chalk hills are common in both the North and the South Downs but a double gap, such as the one at Corfe, is most unusual. It is believed that the two small streams may well have originated on a high level plain which was cut by the sea across Purbeck several million

Corfe Castle

years ago. These streams maintained their separate courses across the Chalk (united just to the north of where Corfe Castle now stands) throughout a following period of uplift of the land. Lowlands were eroded in the softer rocks to the north and to the south, to form the Purbeck heathlands and the central vale of Purbeck, leaving the harder Chalk to form the Purbeck Hills, with the now well established and remarkable gaps on either side of Corfe Castle.

Corfe Common

Just to the south of the village of Corfe Castle in Purbeck lies the long low ridge of Corfe Common. The Common has lain uncultivated for several hundred years, and forms a marked contrast to the pastoral landscape that surrounds it to the east and west. Much of it is covered with herb-rich grassland, although this has been much invaded by bracken and gorse which gives the Common a wilder, unkempt appearance. In recent times, the National Trust, owners of the Common, have initiated an intensive clearing programme, so that many of its slopes now have a much more open appearance.

Geologically speaking, it is one of a series of quartz grit ridges running through the Wealden Beds which form all of the low-lying vale that runs from Swanage to Worbarrow Bay. The Wealden Beds are made up of clays and sands, and are relatively easily eroded, whilst the quartz grit is much tougher and forms upstanding ridges, such as Corfe Common. At the western end of the main ridge of the Common are some overgrown sand pits that provided material for mixing with local Chalk to produce builders' mortar. A series of deep furrows cross the ridge from south to north, giving it an almost corrugated appearance. These have been worn down into the ridge in medieval times as sledges bearing Purbeck Marble were hauled across the Common from the quarries in the south to the stonemasons' workshops in Corfe Castle.

Creechbarrow

Seen from the water meadows of the River Frome at Wareham, Creechbarrow appears as an almost conical feature rising above the thickly wooded country to the south of Stoborough. The view from its summit embraces most of the Isle of Purbeck and extends to the heights of Bulbarrow and Melbury Hill to the north, the distant wooded skyline of the New Forest to the east, and Hardy Monument beyond

Corfe Common

Creechbarrow

Dorchester in the west. It is separated from the Chalk ridge of the Purbeck Hills to the south by the col that carries the narrow road from Creech Grange to East Creech. Creechbarrow itself is built of grits, sands (with bands of flints) and clays, overlain by a thin layer of limestone. The sands and clays are exposed, together with fragments of flint, in the narrow track that leads up to the grassy summit with its triangulation point. The poor soils of its lower slopes are covered with gorse and bracken, contrasted with the tussocky grass that grows on the richer limestone soils on the summit. At greater depth beneath Creechbarrow are seams of ball clay, which have been worked in the past from a series of drift mines driven into the lower slopes of the hill.

The East Chaldon Valley

East Chaldon is one of South Dorset's more remote villages, reached by the minor road from Winfrith Newburgh, or the two narrow roads that run south from the Wareham to Dorchester road before it reaches Owermoigne. It lies on the southern side of an oval-shaped lowland, about ½ mile (800 metres) across and a mile long (1.6 km) drained by the little stream that flows northeast towards Winfrith. The Cretaceous rocks of the East Chaldon Valley have been tightly folded. Such structures are vulnerable to erosion by

The East Chaldon Valley

rain and streams, since folding tends to fracture and weaken the rocks involved. The higher parts of the East Chaldon fold, formed of Chalk and Upper Greensand have been eroded away to reveal the softer clays of the Wealden Beds. The less resistant clays have further encouraged erosion, thus widening the valley into the small lowland. It is surrounded by a steep Chalk escarpment both to the north (which the narrow roads negotiate in sharp bends), and to the south, where the Chalk of High Chaldon forms a dramatic landscape feature. Within the main fold of East Chaldon lies another smaller and older fold, which brings much older Jurassic Limestones to the surface about ½ mile (800 metres) to the north of Grange Dairy.

Giant's Grave Bottom

This unusual valley is cut deeply into the Chalk of the eastern Purbeck Hills, just below their highest point in Godlingston Hill. It begins in a steep combe and then runs southeast for nearly 400 yards (360 metres) and then makes an abrupt turn to continue its course towards the northeast for another 300 yards (275 metres). It eventually joins another dry valley that heads farther to the north under Dean Hill. This main valley runs southeast towards the little village of Ulwell and then follows a course southeast through the northern outskirts of Swanage. Here it is occupied by a small stream that eventually enters the sea at Swanage Bay through a culvert. It is likely that the whole valley system once carried surface drainage, but all of the upper part of the Ulwell Valley and Giant's Grave Bottom are now dry. Giant's Grave Bottom is remarkably steep-sided and was almost certainly cut in the Ice Age, when Purbeck had a tundra climate, similar to that experienced in northern latitudes today. During this time spring meltwaters from the snowfields on Godlingston Hill would have coursed down, cutting deeply into the flanks of the Chalk ridge. During the winter, frost action would have broken up the Chalk in the valley bottom, thus facilitating more erosion in the

Giant's Grave Bottom

following spring and summer. The sudden change in direction of the valley clearly poses some important questions about its development. It is possible that the valley may have originally been opened up by spring action during a warmer period before the Ice Age. Springs tend to open up valley heads and work back along lines of weakness, possibly fault lines in the Chalk, or along major cracks or joints. One line of weakness may account for the lower part of the valley, as far as the abrupt bend, and it is likely that the spring may have then migrated along another line of weakness running from northwest to southeast to account for the upper part of the valley. Thus the course of the valley may have been determined in pre-glacial times, and its steep sides owe their origin to the rapid erosion in the glacial period.

The Golden Bowl

The Golden Bowl is one of the most secret and intimate parts of Purbeck. It occupies the great embayment of land around Encombe House, bounded on the west by the soaring heights of Swyre Head, and on the east by the long flat-topped ridge that runs out from Kingston to Houns-

tout Cliff. The Golden Bowl is a damp and fertile lowland underlain everywhere by the grey shales of the Kimmeridge Clay. The steep slopes that lead up to Swyre Head and the Kingston-Houns-tout ridge are made up of Portland Sand and Portland Stone. Within these slopes there are some interesting hollows, which appear to have been the work of patches of snow and ice that may have accumulated there during the Ice Age. Within the Bowl itself there are two features of interest. Just to the west of Encombe House, there is a well-marked and distinctive mound, capped by gravel deposits. This would appear to be an erosion remnant, with the gravels representing stony material that had been moved down from the surrounding heights during the Ice Age. The second feature is the little stream that flows through the two ornamental lakes to the south of Encombe House, and then through the tangled wood of South Gwyle to Freshwater Steps, where it tips into the sea over a 30-foot (9 metre) waterfall. An alternative origin for the gravels capping the mound may be that they were deposited by this small stream, when it followed a much earlier course to the west of Encombe House. Hummocky mounds below Swyre Head represent landslipping of the Portland Beds over the underlying Kimmeridge Clay.

The Golden Bowl

Hartland Moor

Hartland Moor is one of the largest remaining expanses of heathland in the Isle of Purbeck. It lies between Soldiers Road on the west and the road that runs from Corfe Castle to Arne on the east. The highest point on the moor is Great Knoll that rises to just over 100 feet (30 metres). From this hillock the land falls away to the north and to the south, and these two broad open valleys are drained by peaty streams that flow into Middlebere Lake, a narrow arm of Poole Harbour. Hartland Moor is everywhere underlain by the sands and clays of the Poole Formation, although superficial thicknesses of peat are found in the bottom of the two main valleys. When Poole Harbour was formed during the post-glacial rise in sea level, the streams draining into it began to deposit considerable thicknesses of alluvium in their valley bottoms, and peat began to develop in these waterlogged conditions. The damp valley bottoms and the drier upper slopes have given rise to two quite distinct habitats on Hartland Moor. The valley floors of the two streams show markedly different habitat environments, both of which are dominated by mosses: the northern one is typically acidic, whilst the southern one is alkaline, probably the result of it being fed by water draining from the Chalk to the south. This results in two different plant associations in the two valley bottoms, but where the two streams meet, plants from both the different associations occur together. In these valley bottoms both cross-leaved heather and the rare Dorset Heath are found, in marked contrast to the bell and ling heather that are found on the higher and drier slopes.

The Purbeck 'Gwyles'

'Gwyle' is an old Purbeck word meaning a steep-sided narrow valley. Such features are quite common along the south coast of Purbeck. Some of the streams, such as those at Chapman's Pool, Freshwater Steps below Encombe House, the two valleys that drain into Kimmeridge Bay, and the Lutton Valley at Tyneham, carry small streams. Others such as the valley at Durlston Country Park, and the valleys at Seacombe and Winspit, carry no stream at present, but bear all the evidence of having been eroded by water in the relatively recent past. In a recent wet spell (January 1998), both the Seacombe and Winspit gwyles carried a stream, the result of a rise in the water table consequent upon heavy and continuous rain for two or three weeks.

Hartland Moor

A Purbeck 'gwyle': the valley above Chapman's Pool

Some of the gwyles drain directly into the sea, such as the one at Chapman's Pool and the one at Worbarrow Bay, while others, such as the Freshwater Steps stream, and the eastern Kimmeridge Bay stream, reach sea level over a waterfall. Some of these valleys, particularly the dry examples, end abruptly at the cliff face some 30 feet (9 metres) above the sea. Many of these gwyles show an inner valley cut within a broader more open valley, known as 'valley-in-valley form'. It is generally thought that erosion in these valleys has responded to erosion by the sea along the coast. As the sea has cut back the coast, so the streams have had to cut into their valleys to adjust to the new line of the coast. Successful streams have been able to cut right down to sea level, whilst the others have only managed partial adjustment, and these valleys are left 'hanging' some height above sea level.

Redcliffe

As the River Frome is crossed at South Bridge, Wareham, there are few features of any prominence to be seen across the water meadows stretching away towards Stoborough. However, one salient landmark does hold the attention – the tree-capped low ridge that runs towards the river at

Redcliffe

Redcliffe. Close to the river itself, the ridge ends in a vertical face of rock, cut in red and yellow sandstones and pebble beds. Such rocks underlie considerable areas of the Purbeck heathlands, and are responsible elsewhere for residual erosion features such as the Agglestone. At Redcliffe a riverside path separates the well-marked cliff from the Frome but it is very likely that the Frome at one stage flowed right against Redcliffe, and thus was responsible for the erosional steepening of the northern face of the feature. When rivers meander across their floodplains they migrate from side to side as they move downstream, and thus trim up the higher ground that lies at the limit of the meander belt. Redcliffe is perhaps unusual in that it occurs so far down the course of the Frome, barely 2 miles (3km) from the point where the river enters Poole Harbour. In common with many rivers in their lower course the Frome downstream from Wareham is endyked, and thus free migration of the meanders is no longer possible. Further modification of Redcliffe by the river is unlikely and thus it will remain as an isolated erosion remnant in the marshy landscape that extends from Wareham to Poole Harbour. The remarkable sandstone and pebble beds exposed in Redcliffe are of enduring interest to the geologist, since they tell us a great deal about the evolution of the area some 40 million years ago, when a vast river, much bigger than the present Frome, emptied its waters into a Tertiary sea which covered much of southeast England.

THE COAST

Black Ven

Just over a mile (1.5km) to the east of Lyme Regis lies the 475 feet (144 metres) high cliff of Black Ven. Its cliffs display the largest landslide complex in Western Europe. Much of the lower part of the cliff is made up of dark Jurassic clays and marls, and the upper part is made of contrasting yellow Upper Greensand. Water readily passes down through the permeable Greensand, but cannot pass through the impermeable rocks below. In wet weather, mudslides develop in the clay and marls in the lower cliff, and these move downwards and spill out over the beach below. As a result of the instability in the lower cliff, the upper part of Black Ven is also affected and cracks develop along the cliff-top, and great blocks of Upper Greensand eventually collapse in a series of landslides. The coastal path along the cliff has been disrupted and has had to be diverted inland. Lyme Regis golf course has also lost some of its land as a result of the instability of Black Ven.

Black Ven

Golden Cap

Golden Cap, at 626 feet (191 metres), is the highest point on the Dorset coast, and is a familiar landmark from many points of view along the coast both to the east and the west. It derives its name principally from its capping of Cretaceous Upper Greensand.

The Upper Greensand on Golden Cap consists of an upper section of cherty beds, which rest on the so-called Foxmould, which is made up of yellowish sands, and it is the latter that are responsible for the distinctive colour that is so clearly recognisable from distant view points. Most of Golden Cap, however, is made up of Lower Jurassic sands and clays, and because of the instability of the clays, landslides are an important feature on the middle and lower slopes of the

Golden Cap

headland. Most of the cliff face shows evidence of old land-slides. At the base of the cliffs boulder arcs can be seen at low tide, representing the position of old slips from which much of the finer material has now been eroded away. More recent slides that have extended down to sea level have formed an important barrier to the movement of beach material around the headland. Prominent sandstone bands, such as the Three Tiers Band, are responsible for the almost vertical slopes that characterise some of the middle slopes of Golden Cap.

Chesil Beach

Chesil Beach is a huge bank of shingle that links the Isle of Portland to the mainland to the west. Although opinions differ as to its western limit, it may conveniently be regarded as extending as far west as West Bay – a total distance of over 18 miles (29km). For 8 miles (13km) it encloses the shallow lagoon of The Fleet, which is open to the sea at its eastern end at Ferrybridge. The beach increases in height from 22 feet (7 metres) at Abbotsbury to nearly 50 feet (15 metres) at Chiswell on Portland. It also increases in width to the east from over 300 feet (91 metres) at West Bay to over 800 feet (240 metres) at Wyke Regis. However its most astonishing feature is the grading of the size of the pebbles from west to east. At West Bay the shingle is pea-sized, but it increases to cobble-size at Chiswell. Folklore tells us that fishermen, when landing on the beach in mist or fog, could always tell their whereabouts by the size of the pebbles. Today it is

Chesil Beach

thought that there is not a steady increase in pebble size from west to east, and that on any one stretch of the beach there may be a considerable variation in the size of pebbles on the front of the beach facing the sea. As yet there is no completely satisfactory explanation of the grading of pebble size on the beach. The origin of Chesil Beach is still imperfectly understood. Today it is thought that the beach may have developed well to the south of its present position, during a period of low sea level during the Ice Age. All of Lyme Bay would have been dry land, and the small rivers draining into the bay today would have deposited sizeable aprons of sand and gravel in the area. With rising sea levels in post-glacial times the advancing sea would have swept up these deposits and slowly pushed them landwards to eventually form the present beach.

The Fleet

The Fleet

The Fleet is a unique feature of Dorset's western coast. It is a tidal lagoon that extends from Small Mouth, to the southwest of Wyke Regis, for over 8 miles (13 kilometres) to the northwest at Abbotsbury. The lagoon varies in width from 300 feet (90 metres) at the Narrows to over 3000 feet (915 metres) at Littlesea and Butterstreet Cove. It is over 10 feet (3 metres) deep in the eastern part between Ferrybridge and The Narrows, but becomes much shallower to the west, where it is often less than 3 feet (1 metre) deep. It is thought that it was originally formed as a body of water that was impounded by Chesil Beach, as the latter was gradually pushed shorewards during the post-glacial period. Since then it has gradually been filled with sediment fed in by the numerous small streams that drain the farmland on the landward side of The Fleet. Peat deposits from a much wider Fleet can often be seen on the seaward side of Chesil Beach, indicating that the beach is gradually moving shorewards, thus exposing the ancient peat deposits originally laid down in The Fleet. The present low cliffs around Langton Herring seem to be cut into a

bench that is probably the remnant of a much higher shoreline, cut when the sea level was much higher during the warmer periods during the Ice Age. Although The Fleet is locally quite saline, it is remarkable that there is little salt marsh development. Ecologically, however, The Fleet is both rich and diverse. The eastern Fleet is remarkably different from the shallow lagoon to the northwest; in the east the pebble and boulder floor of The Fleet encourages sponges and invertebrates, whilst further to the west the shallow mud-covered bed provides ideal conditions for the growth of extensive Sea Grass meadows.

Portland Bill

Portland Bill is one of the great landmarks of the Dorset coast. It marks the southernmost extremity of the limestone block of the Isle of Portland, extending out towards the shipping lanes of the English Channel. The limestone mass of Portland is all that remains of the southern limb of a huge upfold in the rocks of the centre of the Dorset coast that was a product of earth movements that occurred about twenty million years ago. On Portland, the limestone remnant dips gently southwards from the heights at the northern end of the island to the Bill where it meets the sea in low cliffs and rocky platforms. The main features of

Portland Bill

geological interest at Portland Bill are the two raised beaches, evidence of higher sea levels in the recent past. The raised beach on the western side of the Bill is best seen capping the cliffs just to the north of Pulpit Rock. This beach is probably over 200,000 years old, and was formed when the sea level was some 47 feet (14.5 metres) higher than it is at present. Higher sea levels at that time were the result of a warmer interglacial period during the Ice Age. Higher temperatures caused some of the ice to melt, with a consequent rise in sea level. On the eastern side of the Bill there are fragments of a lower raised beach, approximately 32 feet (10 metres) above present sea level, probably formed some 125,000 years ago.

Redcliff Point

Redcliff Point lies at the southeastern end of the stretch of landslipped coast that extends from Bowleaze Cove to the Point. Most of this coast is formed by the Corallian Beds, but as Redcliff Point is approached, faulting brings up an important wedge of Oxford Clay at the Point itself. The cliffs of the Point itself are much affected by landslipping,

Redcliff Point

White Nothe

and mudflows extend out on to the beach in a series of lobate outcrops. The name, Redcliff Point, derives its origin from the Red Nodule Bed within the Oxford Clay, which outcrops at the Point itself, and tends to be particularly distinctive. It is faulted against the grey Nothe Clay of the overlying Corallian Beds. Immediately to the east of Redcliff Point the Corallian Beds are folded up into the Ham Hill anticline, where the prominent dips in the strata form a clear feature in the cliffs. Beneath the cliffs of Redcliff Point itself is an interesting recurved spit, formed of sand and shingle as it is carried round the Point.

White Nothe

White Nothe is the most westerly bastion of the Chalk in Dorset; it does not reappear again until the cliffs of Beer in Devon are reached. It dominates all of the coast to the east of Weymouth and represents the beginning of the stretch of coastline to the east where the Chalk is a major feature intermittently as far east as Worbarrow Bay. In common with the Chalk cliff outcrops to the east in Worbarrow Bay and Swanage Bay, much of the cliff profile is dominated by landslides. The Chalk is underlain by the unstable beds of the Gault, which in its turn rests on the Kimmeridge Clay. This juxtaposition of rocks has meant that the Gault and

Kimmeridge Clay are unable to support the weight of the overlying Chalk and Upper Greensand, and thus huge landslips occur on the face of White Nothe and it overlooks a vast undercliff formed of the remains of past landslides. Just to the west of White Nothe there is an interesting exposure of the Portland and Purbeck Beds in the cliffs below Holworth House, although these beds are also rendered unstable by the underlying Kimmeridge Clay. The Kimmeridge Clay cliffs still carry the name of Burning Cliff, which originated from the spontaneous combustion within the oil shales noted in 1826, which continued for several years afterwards.

Scratchy Bottom

This unusual valley meets the coast some 600 feet (182 metres) to the west of Durdle Door. The valley is about ½ mile (800 metres) long from its head near Newlands Farm to the point where it meets the coast, above the sand and shingle beach to the west of Durdle Door. In its upper section it trends approximately east–west, but about halfway along its length it turns through a right angle, and the remainder of its course to the sea follows a north–south orientation. This change in direction of the valley may have resulted from the spring at the valley head cutting back along joint directions at right angles to one another. Scratchy Bottom is a steep-sided valley, but it is distinctively flat-bottomed, particularly in its lower reaches. It is a valley that is truncated at the coast, with the valley bottom ending abruptly some 50 feet (15 metres) above the beach below – the result of rapid cliff retreat. Although the valley is cut in Upper Chalk through-out its length, superficial deposits are exposed along its sides, and in the valley bottom in the cliff profile where it meets the coast, and there is no reason to suppose that these deposits do not continue inland. These deposits are probably the result of solifluction, when loose surface debris sludged

Scratchy Bottom

down the valley sides during the brief periglacial summer, during the Ice Age. Scratchy Bottom is a dry valley, which probably has not been drained by a stream since late periglacial times. During the cold conditions of a periglacial climate deep frost shattering of the Chalk would have taken place, enabling a stream to readily erode the fragmented Chalk during the brief summer. In periglacial times the Chalk, deeply frozen under permafrost conditions, would have been impermeable, thus encouraging surface drainage. After periglacial times, when the Chalk again became permeable, Scratchy Bottom would have dried out.

The Lulworth Coast

This section of the Dorset coast, which extends from Worbarrow Bay in the east to Bat's Head in the west, is almost certainly the most frequently visited. It is renowned for its distinctive geology, and has long been regarded as one of the most important sites for the teaching of coastal land-form development in the world. It is essentially a concor-dant coastline with the strata running parallel with the coast. The relatively hard and resistant beds of the Portland Limestone are the most southerly of the strata in this section of the coast, although they have been eroded away between Worbarrow Tout and Mupe Rocks in the east, and between Dungy Head and the Durdle Promontory in the west. Northwards the Purbeck Beds, the Wealden Beds, the Upper Greensand and the Chalk outcrop in that order. The Wealden Beds are the least resistant to erosion of the rocks in this sequence, and this is a key factor of landform devel-opment on this stretch of coast. Once the hard barrier of the Portland Limestone has been breached, marine erosion can erode away the Purbeck Beds, and more particularly, the Wealden Beds, more readily. It was once thought that Stair Hole to the immediate west of Lulworth Cove, where this process is most easily observed, was the type model for this aspect of coastal development. Today this is no longer thought to be the case. Lulworth Cove partly owes its

development to the work of the small stream that enters the cove on its western side. In the past this stream cut its way through the gap in the Portland Limestone that now forms the entrance to the cove, allowing the sea ready access to the weaker rocks to the north in the period of post-glacial rise in sea level. Subsequent erosion opened up the near perfect semicircular cove. It is thought by some that Worbarrow Bay and Mupe Bay in the east, and St Oswald's Bay, Man O' War Bay and Durdle Cove in the west may have developed in a similar way, although important differences exist between each of these examples.

Above: *Lulworth Cove and Stair Hole*
Left: *Mupe Bay*

Gad Cliff

This long and precipitous feature is one of the outstanding landmarks of the Purbeck coast, and can be seen clearly from as far away as the Isle of Portland. It forms a spectacular backdrop to the neatly carved Kimmeridge Bay to the east. 'Gad' is an old Purbeck quarryman's term for one of the wedges or tools used in the stone trade, and it is the remarkable resemblance of the sharp profile of Gad Cliff to these tools that has given the cliff its name. Gad Cliff extends east-west from near Tyneham Cap to the tiny inlet of Pondfield Cove just to the east of Worbarrow Bay. Geologically speaking the cliff is made up of Portland Stone overlying Portland Sand, which in turn rests on Kimmeridge Clay. This is a classic landslip situation, seen elsewhere along this coast at Houns-tout, Emmetts Hill and St Aldhelm's Head and also along the northern side of the Isle of Portland. Water percolates down through the permeable Portland Stone and the Portland Sand, but fails to enter the impermeable Kimmeridge Clay below, and begins to seep out at this point. This renders much of the underlying Kimmeridge Clay unstable, and thus it is unable to bear the weight of the overlying Portland Stone and Portland Sand. Huge rota-tional slips develop as a result of this underlying instability, and this has resulted in the continual development of fresh rock faces in the topmost Portland Stone. Much of the lower part of Gad Cliff is thus a tumbled undercliff composed of the remnants of past landslips. These landslips are largely overgrown by impenetrable thickets of black-thorn, and thus this section of coast has become one of the most inaccessible in the whole of Dorset.

The Kimmeridge Coast and the Ledges

Cliffs of Kimmeridge Clay extend for some 3 miles (5km) to the east of Kimmeridge Bay as far as Houns-tout, and for a mile or so to the west as far as Brandy Bay. The Kimmeridge Clay is a formation made up principally of shales, within which there is a series of harder limestone bands known as cementstones. Apart from around Kimmeridge Bay, where the cliffs are relatively low, the high shale cliffs run unbroken eastwards as far as Freshwater Steps, where the stream from South Gwyle below Encombe House reaches the sea by a spectacular waterfall. Similarly the shale cliffs form fairly high features as far west as the limits of Brandy Bay. The cliffs everywhere are quite unstable, particularly after long periods

Gad Cliff from the west

The Kimmeridge Coast and the Ledges

of rain in winter, and are much prone to slipping. Even in dry periods in summer, shale fragments are continually cascading down the face of the cliffs.

As a result of the slight upfold or anticline which makes its appearance in Kimmeridge Bay, the shales and cementstones in the bays to the west dip towards the west. To the east of the bay the shales and cementstones dip towards the east, whilst in the bay itself the beds have very low dips. The cementstones form some of the most distinctive scenery on this section of the Dorset coast. Where the dips are relatively low, as at Broad Bench just to the west of Kimmeridge Bay, the cementstones, such as The Flats Stone Band, at the foot of the cliffs form almost horizontal ledges. Where there is greater dip, as in Brandy Bay to the west and the long stretch of cliffs to the east, the bands form important rock ribs that run out to sea for several hundred yards. These are, of course, a tremendous hazard to shipping, with the loss of the S.S. *Treveal* in January 1920 being the most tragic of the shipwrecks.

Chapman's Pool

Lying between the huge limestone-capped mass of Hounstout and the vertical cliffs and tumbled landslides of Emmetts Hill, Chapman's Pool is one of Purbeck's most distinctive coastal features. The sheltered bay is backed by

Chapman's Pool

cliffs of unstable Kimmeridge Clay, and the entrance is fringed by large boulders that are the remnants of landslides on both Houns-tout and Emmetts Hill. Kimmeridge Clay is not particularly resistant to wave erosion, and thus the sea has been able to carve this small bay out of the valley that separates the higher land on either side. Two small streams, one rising in West Hill Bottom itself, meet to flow into the eastern side of the pool. In order to keep pace with marine erosion in the pool, both streams have incised their valleys deeply. On occasions, landslides from Emmetts Hill block the lower part of the stream and valley, and the ponded-back waters have to cut a new channel to the pool. At low tide ledges of Kimmeridge shale are exposed along the foreshore, where examples of the rich ammonite fauna can be found.

Peveril Point

In the *Hand of Ethelberta* Thomas Hardy described the rocks off Peveril Point, just to the south of Swanage, as a 'sinister ledge of limestone, like a crocodile's teeth'. The sharp reefs are well known to sailors and a major hazard to inshore sailing along the Dorset coast. Peveril Point forms the northern enclosing arm of Durlston Bay, which presents the

Peveril Point

most complete section of the Purbeck Beds along the coast of Dorset, and is indeed the world type-section of the Purbeck succession for geologists. These beds were laid down in shallow lagoonal waters under sub-tropical conditions, and consist mainly of richly fossiliferous thinly-bedded limestones and mudstones. It is the uppermost sequence of the Purbeck Beds that are exposed at Peveril Point. Here the Upper Purbeck Beds are formed of the Broken Shell Limestone, the so-called *Unio* Beds (named after a small mollusc), and the well-known Purbeck Marble Beds. The Upper Purbeck Beds are here folded into a sharp downfold or syncline so that the Broken Shell Limestone appears twice on either side of Peveril Point and forms the two jagged reefs which extend some 295 feet (90 metres) out to sea. Within the two reefs, the *Unio* Beds can be picked out at low tide. In the centre of the downfold a dish-shaped feature marks the outcrop of the Purbeck Marble. It is, of course, not a real marble, but a shelly limestone formed of small freshwater snails, which takes a ready polish, and has been widely used in churches both in Purbeck and farther afield. Many fragments of the distinctive limestone, here weathered to a reddish colour, can be found on the beach.

Old Harry Rocks and The Pinnacles

These sea stacks, off Handfast Point, the most easterly point of the Chalk cliffs of eastern Purbeck, are some of the most familiar features of the World Heritage Site of the Dorset and East Devon coast. The Purbeck Hills meet the western end of Poole Bay in a line of cliffs that extend from Punfield Cove, at the northern end of Swanage Bay to the southern end of South Beach Studland. The cliffs facing Swanage Bay are cut in almost vertical Chalk, but north of the famous Ballard Down fault, dips on the Chalk begin to decrease, and at Handfast Point the Chalk is dipping gently to the north-west. The Upper Chalk here is both well-bedded and jointed, which means that it is readily susceptible to erosion by waves. An examination of the detached sections of the

Old Harry Rocks and The Pinnacles

Studland Sand Dunes

Studland dunes occupy the eastern half of the South Haven Peninsula, one of the two enclosing arms of Poole Harbour. The dunes are unique amongst the physical landscapes of Dorset since there are no other sizeable areas of similar sand accumulation between Lyme Regis in the west and Highcliffe in the east. Several factors have combined to create this series of arcuate dune ridges that run parallel to the shore of Studland Bay. A ready supply of sand is available from Studland Beach on the seaward side. Easterly winds, blowing in from Poole Bay, sweep up the sand and move it onshore. Although these are not the prevailing winds, which are from the southwest and offshore, the easterlies blow often enough to be a potent force in the supply of sand to the dunes. Once the sand has been moved off the beach it is fixed in position by a number of species of grasses. Although sand couch grass seems to be the first coloniser, it is marram grass which is principally responsible for holding the sand in position with its dense and penetrating root

Chalk beyond Handfast Point will reveal that the sea has eroded along the lines of weakness such as the bedding planes and the joints. Small caves are first produced by wave action, and these later cut right through the Chalk remnants to produce arches such as those in No Man's Land. Collapse of the roof of the arches will lead to the formation of sea stacks, such as Old Harry and The Pinnacles. Erosion of the base of the stacks will result in them only being supported by a narrow plinth of rock which will eventually collapse and the stack will fall. The best example of this is Old Harry's Wife, that succumbed after a major storm in 1896, and only remains as a stump alongside Old Harry. The latter stack is at present undercut in a similar way and awaits the same fate. The Pinnacles, farther to the south along the coast, have much more secure bases and are likely to survive for much longer.

Studland Sand Dunes

system. Once the dunes have been fixed, other species such as sand sedge, hawkbit, sea spurge and sea bindweed begin to appear and form a denser mat of vegetative cover to the dunes. The dune ridges have grown steadily seawards over the last 400 years and today at least four dune ridges can be recognised. From time to time another embryonic ridge may begin to form on the seaward side. Although these latter foredunes were eroded away in the late 1990s, they have recently reappeared after less stormy winters. However, with global warming, rising sea levels and increasing storminess, there may now be a threat to the long-term stability of the dunes.

Little Sea

West of the sand-dune complex that now forms the eastern part of the South Haven Peninsula to the north of Studland lies the enclosed body of water known as Little Sea. All of the sand-dune complex has developed relatively recently in historical time. Beyond Little Sea to the west is an old sea cliff, now much degraded, with the Wildlife Information Centre perched on its crest. This old cliff probably marked the original position of the coastline in about 1600, as shown by Camden's *Britannia* map of 1607. All of the land to the east of that has accumulated over the last 400 years, in a series of dune ridges, the oldest of which is Third Ridge, just to the east of the northern arm of Little Sea, formed by about 1720. The most seaward ridge, oddly enough called Zero Ridge, began to form in about 1950. Little Sea itself first appeared on Avery's map in 1721, where it was shown as a tidal inlet partly enclosed to the east by what is today known as Third Ridge. By the end of the eighteenth century, the tidal inlet had become a lagoon and Second Ridge had begun to form. In the mid-nineteenth century, the lagoon had become more enclosed and was only invaded by the sea at the highest spring tides. Today Little Sea is a reed-fringed freshwater lake, about one mile (1.6 kilometres) long and approximately 900 feet (275 metres) wide, linked northwards to Shell Bay by the narrow peaty stream of Central Cut. Its smaller neighbour to the east, Eastern Lake, is similarly connected to the sea by New Cut. Little grebes, moorhens and mute swans breed on the shores of Little Sea and in winter there may be as many as 3000 ducks on its waters, including pintail and pochard. The tranquil waters of Little Sea, with their distinctive wildlife, today form the centrepiece of the Studland National Nature Reserve, managed by English Nature.

Hengistbury Head

Seen from either Christchurch Bay to the east or Poole Bay to the west, Hengistbury Head is a prominent coastal landmark. It is a low gravel-capped headland, with cliffs up to 118 feet (36 metres), separated from the main plateaux on which Bournemouth is built to the west by a narrow neck of land between Poole Bay and Christchurch Harbour. Hengistbury Head is composed of Tertiary sands and clays, with a gravel capping of younger age, all relatively soft rocks that are very susceptible to erosion. A striking feature of the cliff profile is the marked bands of ironstone or 'doggers', fallen blocks of which form an apron of debris at the foot of

Little Sea

Hengistbury Head

Mudeford Sandspit

Mudeford Sandspit is the larger of two features that almost enclose Christchurch Harbour on the seaward side, leaving the combined Stour and Avon to reach the sea through the narrow exit called The Run. The sand and shingle spit extends north-northeastwards from Hengistbury Head and has been built from beach material that has been brought by longshore drift round the end of Hengistbury Head. Over a period of thousands of years waves from the east have built this material into the present-day spit.

It has a reputation of being one of the most mobile of Dorset's coastal features. In the past it has had a tendency to grow steadily northeastwards and at a time in the 1880s, and again in the early 1900s, its far (or distal) end reached a point opposite Highcliffe Castle. Frontal attack by easterly storms has resulted in the breaching of the spit near its roots on a number of occasions (in 1883, 1911, 1924 and 1935). After the last of these breachings the distal end became detached and gradually drifted inshore towards Friars Cliff, enclosing a lagoon in the late 1930s.

the cliff. The ironstone boulders form a natural line of defence against marine erosion, and their removal by a local mining company for a period in the mid-nineteenth century had the disastrous effect of increasing the rate of cliff erosion once the blocks were removed.

Within a period of some eighty years nearly half of the headland was lost to the sea, a matter of great concern for local people. In order to stabilise the situation, the Long Groyne at the eastern end of Hengistbury Head was built in order to prevent the drift of sand and shingle eastwards and thus stabilising the beaches beneath the cliffs. This proved to be highly effective as a wide beach became established at the foot of the headland, with the accumulation of sand leading to the build-up of dunes immediately to the west of the groyne. The adverse effect of the building of the groyne was to starve the coast beyond the groyne of the sediment that was now trapped to the west. This led to increased erosion of the easternmost parts of the headland and to the destabilising of Mudeford Sandspit, both of which have necessitated additional defence works along this section of the coast.

As a result of the building of the Long Groyne at Hengistbury Head in 1938–39, the spit became unstable again, since renewing beach material was arrested in its movement around the point of the Head. Without this material the spit began to suffer under continued wave attack from the east. Numerous attempts have been made to stabilise the spit in the second half of the twentieth century. Small seawalls were built to protect the most vulnerable parts of the spit in the 1960s, and in the last twenty years a series of rubble groynes have been constructed in order to encourage a wider beach to develop. Much of the spit now carries beach chalets, commanding substantial sums of money when they change hands, and this has made the continued protection of the spit a very high priority in coastal protection policy.

Mudeford Sandspit